THE MASSACRE OF PETERLOO

The Massacre of Peterloo

A dramatization of the massacre which occurred
in Manchester on August 16th 1819

by

John Hipkin

HEINEMANN EDUCATIONAL BOOKS
LONDON

Heinemann Educational Books Ltd
LONDON EDINBURGH MELBOURNE AUCKLAND TORONTO
SINGAPORE HONG KONG KUALA LUMPUR
IBADAN NAIROBI JOHANNESBURG
NEW DELHI

ISBN 0 435 23700 4

*All rights whatsoever in this play are
strictly reserved and all applications for
permission to perform it must be made in
advance to*

Heinemann Educational Books Ltd
(Drama Department)
The Press at
Kingswood
Tadworth, Surrey

Published by
Heinemann Educational Books Ltd
48 Charles Street, London W1X 8AH
Printed Offset Litho and bound in Great Britain by
Cox & Wyman Ltd, London, Fakenham and Reading

CONTENTS

ACKNOWLEDGEMENT

The author and publisher wish to thank David Higham Associates, and William Collins Sons & Co Ltd for permission to reproduce the extract from *Fame is the Spur* by Howard Spring.

INTRODUCTION

The Massacre of Peterloo has been written for senior boys and girls in the secondary school. The final cast could well comprise up to two hundred performers, though producers will find it easier to start rehearsals with the small number of 'principals' in the preliminary scenes and gradually 'phase in' to the larger crowd scenes. Handling two hundred pupils in one room is no easy undertaking though by the time this scale of rehearsal is in operation most of the cast will recognize the need for control and discipline since the performance itself can only be a matter of a few days off.

The Massacre of Peterloo also offers an exceptional opportunity for a comprehensive school project allied to the dramatic production. The second section of this book, entitled *Project Peterloo*, contains a number of suggestions as to how such a project might be mounted.

A Historical Note

On August 16th 1819, a crowd of Manchester working-people, variously estimated at between sixty and a hundred thousand, gathered, in almost festive mood, on the field adjoining St Peter's Church. This enormous and orderly demonstration, organized by local Radical Unions, had been convened to demand representation in Parliament for the people of Manchester. The meeting had scarcely begun when it was assaulted by detachments of the Manchester Yeomanry and the 15th King's Hussars who proceeded to cut down the defenceless participants.

This play describes that fateful day and traces the sequence of events which led to its climax: the wounding or killing of some 500 men, women and children. It attempts to show that those responsible for the decision to disperse the crowd by force were motivated more by fear than malice, and that the demonstrators, far from being dangerous revolutionaries, were really amateurs when it came to political agitation. What worried the magistrates was the unusual orderliness of the assembly. They mistook it for a military exercise rather than as an attempt by the workers to impress the authorities with how self-disciplined and reasonable they were; how ready, in short, to share in the political life of their country.

The impulse to march to the Manchester meeting was an urgent one, born of frustration and injustice. The Radical leaders believed that life would be more tolerable if only representation in Parliament could be gained. Although their demands were resisted and the Manchester meeting itself ended in disaster, Peterloo initiated a series of reforms culminating in the Representation of the People Act, 1928, when every man and woman in the country was finally granted the right to vote. It also helped to establish the labour movement which today finds expression in important organizations like the Trades Unions, the Co-operative Societies and the popular political parties.

At a time when the elementary rights which we as a society have won for ourselves are still denied to so large a section of mankind, the story of the Massacre of Peterloo may help us to recommit ourselves to the vital principle of liberty and the rights of men and women everywhere to forge their own destiny under its protection.

(Producers may find it helpful to include this brief note in programmes distributed to audiences).

Production Notes

'Peterloo' needs space, the more the better. The size of the audience is almost a secondary consideration. It is a play in the round. The audience, which is not likely to exceed a couple of hundred per performance, should be seated along the sides of the hall, their seating somewhat angled towards the stage where most of the preliminary scenes will be played. This should leave an extensive 'acting area' comprising the major portion of the hall itself, the stage, and any easily accessible parts off, such as foyers and corridors. In order to arrange the large crowd and drilling scenes in the play it is essential that the producer integrate as much of the surrounding area as possible into the production. The plan on page xiii demonstrates this need in visual terms, though it is recognized that facilities will vary greatly from school to school.

Timing and discipline are the essential features of the production. There should be close and continuous communication between the actors who are on and those awaiting their entrances. During these waiting periods absolute silence and stillness must be achieved. Much of the play's impact depends upon the unexpected but orderly arrival of large numbers of people. The crowds must learn to alternate between calm immobility before arrival and animated activity once they have entered into the main action. Herein lies one of the principal educative strengths of the play.

It will be advisable to phase rehearsals. The total production period need not exceed six or seven weeks. Certainly the play and the project work which can surround it could be completed in half a term. During the first week or two the principal parts should be allocated. No single part should take longer than a few days to learn. Producers will have their own opinions about when parts should be learned in relation to first rehearsals. There are certainly very great advantages in getting children to be word perfect before any rehearsing begins, especially as movement is more easily practised if actors are free of the impediment of scripts held in the hand. These early rehearsals can all take place on stage and the play is deliberately structured to allow the separate scenes to be tackled in isolation. They can be easily fitted in according to the availability of different individuals and teams of actors.

In the third week an 'embryonic' crowd should be selected and their drilling and marching started. Boys and girls can rehearse much of this in spare time, during the lunch hour or for a few minutes after school. This small crowd will become the practised core to which later additions can be made as the production proceeds and develops. The full crowd need not be mobilized until a few days before the actual time of public performance. Once the whole cast has gained the confidence of knowing what it has to do and when it must be done, there should be at least two full-dress rehearsals. By this time the lighting technicians, scene-hands and sound effect technicians should be fully incorporated into the production. A further description of how rehearsals might be arranged appears in *Project Peterloo*.

A Note on Dialect

The Massacre of Peterloo took place in the very heart of Manchester. Those principally involved were Lancashire folk. The language they used had its own distinctive phraseology, vocabulary, and sound. To have written this play in that dialect would have created serious problems for children outside Lancashire. It was therefore decided to write it in a 'neutral' style, understandable to children throughout the country. Of course it will add a great deal to the play if those who perform it use their own local and authentic dialects. After all the language of liberty is at once local and universal.

The Music

The following Parts of the play require the inclusion of music:

Part One: The CLERGYMAN's entrance is accompanied by organ music; his departure by hymn-singing.
The opening speeches of the MAGISTRATE and the RADICAL are preceded by trumpet fanfares or drum-rolls.

Part Two: Kate and Tom enter to the distant sound of dancing music. Producers are strongly advised to consider 'The Weavers' March' which may be heard on side two of 'The Iron Muse',

TOPIC RECORD 12T86, obtainable from Topic Records Ltd, 27 Nassington Road, London N.W.3. 'The Poor Cotton Way-ver' and other songs connected with the Lancashire textile industry are included on this same record.

Part Three: Jane's little dance fantasy might be accompanied by one of the lively tunes from 'The Iron Muse'.

Part Four: The early attempts at marching can be accompanied by a single drum rapping out a marching beat. The final march should either be led by an actual brass band or accompanied by recorded brass band music.

Part Six: The entry of the CROWD and the later entry of HENRY HUNT should be accompanied by triumphal brass band music. As for the end of this scene, the Eleventh Symphony, '1905' by SHOSTAKOVITCH is ideal. If the first movement is begun at the point where the REPORTER says, 'It was a terrible, terrible day' the mood lasts right until Samuel is brought home. This passage is very subdued and may need to be played quite loudly. The only recording of this symphony is on Columbia 33CX 1604.

Part Eight: The parade of banners will be accompanied by the playing of 'We Shall Overcome'. The entire cast sings the song as a finale.

Please note: Licences for the public performance of records should be obtained from:

Phonographic Performances Ltd.
Evelyn House, 62 Oxford Sreet, London, W.1.

PLAN OF THE SET

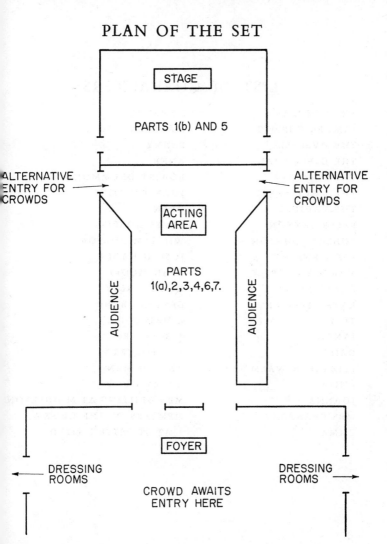

Producers may find this model helpful even though their own resources are likely to be very different. Some may even wish to abandon this lay-out and 'build' the play quite differently.

LIST OF CHARACTERS

THE SCHOLAR

SAMUEL COPPITT

THE OVERSEER

THE CLERGYMAN

THE PRISONER

THE MAGISTRATE

THE RADICAL

PETER SAXTON

ROBERT JOHNSON

JOHN KNIGHT

MARTHA COPPITT

AGNES COPPITT

KATE FARLEIGH

TOM

JANE

DAISY

ELIZABETH WALMSLEY

EMILY

JOANNA

MRS CRANFORD

EMMA

DOROTHY

MAUREEN

FANNY

ANNE

ROBERT DRUMMOND

JOHN PRENTICE

DEAN

JAMES NORRIS

WILLIAM HULTON

JOSEPH NADIN

JOHN MOORE

HUGH BIRLEY

GENERAL BYNG

A MESSENGER

A SOLDIER

A REPORTER

AN OLD MAN

HENRY HUNT

MEN DRILLING AT MIDDLETON

MEMBERS OF THE CROWD
    AT ST PETER'S FIELD

SYNOPSIS

Part One: The kitchen of Samuel Coppitt's house.

Part Two: A street near Kate's house.

Part Three: The George Leigh Union Room, Manchester.

Part Four: A field in Middleton.

Part Five: The Bull Inn, Manchester.

Part Six: St Peter's Fields, Manchester.

Part Seven: The home of Samuel Coppitt.

Part Eight: The hall of the school.

Time: August 16th 1819, and the few preceding days.

This play is dedicated to the pupils of Senacre School, Maidstone, Kent, who performed it first in May 1965.

PART ONE

The audience are seated. House lights dim. Two low boxes or platforms are in position, one in the centre of the hall and a second nearer the stage and slightly to the side. A spot picks out the SCHOLAR, *a member of the school presenting the play. He is dressed in the clothes he would normally wear. Under his arm he holds a large folio. Just before proceeding towards his platform at the other end of the hall he bids the audience 'Good Evening'. He walks to and mounts the low platform which stands a few feet before the stage, opens his folio and begins to 'read'.*

SCHOLAR: The play which will be performed this evening is a true and accurate representation of certain events which took place in Manchester during the second week of August, 1819. The characters in this drama are real in that they portray people who actually existed or are typical of those who did.

    No man or woman alive today is likely to have known anyone who witnessed the Massacre of Peterloo. Nevertheless there are accounts and records of what happened which are as authentic and vivid as personal memories. There are songs and poems, letters and petitions, drawings and relics, from all of which this drama has been created. (*He pauses.*)

    Let us first try to imagine Manchester as it existed in 1819. One historian tells us: 'It was not so much a town as a barracks, a barracks of an industry, a town grown vast in the short space of fifty years, a mass of mills and damp, mean houses erected with the utmost disregard of everything except immediate profit.'

    For the workman it was a prison from within which one of them bitterly complained: 'The green grass and the healthful hay-field are shut out from our path. The whistling of birds is not for us. We eat the worst food, drink the worst drink – our raiment, our houses, our everything bear signs of poverty.'

Their grievances were many but they went unheeded. Manchester, with a population of 160,000 was not even represented in Parliament. In fact those responsible for the orderly administration of the town were a group of magistrates appointed by the Lord of the Manor who lived at Rolleston Hall in Staffordshire, forty miles from Manchester.

This play is about the people of Manchester and their struggle. It begins at the home of Samuel Coppitt, a handloom weaver.

(*The curtain opens to reveal the dimly-lit kitchen of* SAMUEL COPPITT's *home.* SAMUEL *is at work at his loom which is angled so that the audience do not see his face as yet. There is a stove, a small table and two or three stools.*)

SCHOLAR: Samuel has lived in this house, worked in this dank room for the best part of twenty years. His family have been weavers for a century. As a boy he worked with his father in a cottage in Middleton which was then green and open country.

SAMUEL (*his face and shoulders lit as he turns towards the audience*): It were a decent cottage and well-furnished. There were a mahogany clock and a dresser. We had a small garden which supplied us with vegetables enough for our needs. We never had to go to the Parish for relief.

SCHOLAR: But these golden times did not last. Samuel moved to Manchester and raised his family against the background of war, high rents, low wages, rising prices and increasing mechanization. Two of his sons died in Flanders and a third wasted away with consumption. Now he lives with his wife, Martha, and their only daughter, Agnes, upon whose wages from the mill they depend, for Samuel's income is reduced to a pittance.

Why, you may ask, does Samuel not abandon his dying craft? Are the mills not crying out for labour? True, women and children are needed in abundance, but men cannot find work so easily. Besides, Samuel is no longer young and he is loth to change the pattern of his life. The mills are large, dirty and racked with the noise of engines and machines. They impose a discipline to which Samuel is unaccustomed.

(*At this point an* OVERSEER *enters the hall and walks briskly to the centre where he mounts a platform higher than that of the* SCHOLAR'S. *He faces the stage and reads from a rule book.*)

This man is an overseer in the local mill. He is better paid than his fellow-workers though his privilege lasts only so long as he can extract from them the necessary quotas. He reads now from his rule book. Remember as he reads that few men earned more than 20/– a week in the mills.

OVERSEER: The following offences and negligences are subject to deductions:

Any spinner found with his window open 1/–
Any spinner found dirty at his work 1/–
Any spinner found washing himself 2/–
Any spinner heard whistling 2/–
Any spinner not at work five minutes after last bell rings.... 3/–
Any spinner going further than the roving-room door when fetching rovings 3/–
Any spinner being sick and cannot find another spinner to give satisfaction must pay for steam per day 6/–

(*He dismounts the platform and leaves the hall.*)

SCHOLAR: Samuel and many of his fellow-weavers would starve rather than submit to such rules. Yet despite his misfortunes, Samuel has learned to bear them with patience. Regularly each Sunday he attends the local chapel.

(SAMUEL *leaves his loom and walks to the front of the stage. Chapel organ music is heard. At the same time a* CLERGYMAN *enters and mounts the centre platform. He signals* SAMUEL *to kneel, which he does.*)

CLERGYMAN: We deeply sympathize with those of you, dear Brethren, who, from the pressure of the times, in common with thousands of your countrymen, are involved in various and deep afflictions. We offer up to God for you in this dark season our prayers, that you may not be tempted above what you are able to bear. Remember that in heaven you have a better and enduring substance. Remember you are Christians, and are called by your profession to exemplify the power and influence of religion by your patience in suffering. It is your Christian duty to Fear God and honour the King; to submit to magistrates for conscience' sake and not to speak evil of dignitaries, and above all beware of those who would deceive you into political parties and associations! (*Clasping his hands together.*) Bear your sufferings with fortitude. The Good Lord will not desert you in your hour of need. (*He dismounts and withdraws. As he does so the sound of chapel hymn-singing is heard for a few seconds.* SAMUEL *rises and returns to his loom.*)

SCHOLAR: Our clergyman's warnings were apposite, for many of those 'deceived' into political parties were thrown into prison; but their voice was heard if only to remind those tempted by their example of the consequences which awaited them.

(*A* PRISONER *enters in chains and approaches the centre platform. He kneels before it, his arms outstretched before it in supplication.*)

PRISONER: In behalf of meself and fellow-prisoners who humbly crave your assistance in our present distress, we was taken by the military on Monday, March 10th last, betwixt Manchester and Stockport on our journey for London with an intent of presenting a petition to the Prince Regent, for a redress of our grievances which was dreadful in the extreme, our families being nearly in a state of starvation, and having no means of paying our rents and nearly naked for want of raiment.

We was detained in the New Bailey, Manchester, in the lock-ups for thirteen days and nights with nothing but bare flags to sleep upon which I found affected my health.

We beg leave now, my Lord, to request you release us from this place. Our families, we fear, have need of what little support we might provide and we give your Lordships solemn promise that never again shall we give you cause for complaint.

My Lord, we hope you will take our case into consideration and as we trust in your clemency we rest in hopes we shall not be disappointed. (*He rises laboriously and moves away. Just short of the exit he turns and adds*:) We do assure your Lordship we really thought we was doing our duty as real friends to the laws and constitution of our country. (*He leaves.*)

SCHOLAR: Such were the voices dissuading Samuel from protest. But men cannot indefinitely endure injustice and hardship. Manchester at this time seethed with unrest. A year before, the spinners had struck and were smashed. In January of the same year, Henry Hunt had addressed a vast assembly of working people but Samuel had stayed at home.

Now the Radicals of Manchester planned the greatest of all demonstrations to be held on the open ground adjoining St Peter's Church in the very heart of Manchester. As the date of the meeting drew near the population were assailed with notices and advertisements. The magistrates, fearful of the outcome of this massive gathering, saw fit to issue their own warnings.

(*Two figures now appear at either side of the stage, one a* RADICAL *wearing a cap of liberty and the other a* MAGISTRATE. *Both read from large sheets of paper. Before the Radical begins his first speech he is lit by a spot. The Magistrate is similarly lit when he first speaks. A drum-roll or trumpet fanfare may prelude the opening speeches.*)

RADICAL: Workpeople of Manchester and the surrounding towns and villages! Here is a notice issued this day, August 9th, 1819, by the Patriotic Union Society:

You are respectfully informed that a meeting will be held on Monday, August 16th, 1819, on the area near St Peter's Church, to take into consideration the most speedy and effectual mode of obtaining Radical reform in the Commons House of Parliament.

MAGISTRATE: It has come to the notice of the magistrates of this city that an advertisement in the Manchester *Observer* paper of this day calls for the convening of a public and illegal meeting for

Monday, the 16th August next to be held on the area near St Peter's Church.

RADICAL: We have called this meeting, friends, because we are fully convinced that nothing less than widespread popular protest can remove the intolerable evils under which the people of this country have for so long and still do groan. We shall meet to demand the right to elect a person to represent the inhabitants of Manchester who are denied the vote in Parliament.

MAGISTRATE: The magistrates of this town and for the Counties Palatine of Lancaster and Chester, do hereby caution all persons to abstain from attending such an illegal meeting. Should they attend it will be at their own peril.

RADICAL: You will meet on Monday next, my friends, and by your steady, firm and temperate behaviour, you will convince all your enemies that you feel you have an important and overriding public duty to perform.

MAGISTRATE: The magistrates, the military and the civil authorities of Manchester have found evidence to suggest that the worst possible spirit pervades the country. They are particularly disturbed to learn that considerable numbers have been drilling today in and around Manchester.

RADICAL: You may be sure that our enemies will seek every opportunity to excite a riot next Monday so that they shall have an excuse for spilling our blood. You must come then, my friends, armed with no weapon save a good conscience, determined in no circumstances to commit a breach of the peace.

MAGISTRATE: We hope, of course, that the peace may be preserved but in the circumstances it is scarcely possible to expect it.

(*The two men face one another in silence and defiance for a few seconds. Lights fade.*)

SCHOLAR: The prelude to our play is over. Now Samuel, his wife and daughter, Kate and Tom, the men and women of Manchester hold the stage and tell of that fateful week 150 years ago.

(*He closes his folio and leaves the hall. The light on Samuel's kitchen brightens a little. Within a few seconds the heavy footsteps of the three Radicals can be heard. They enter the hall and knock at Samuel's door.* MARTHA *goes to the door, wiping her hands on her apron. The callers are members of the Middleton Union Society:* PETER SAXTON, ROBERT JOHNSON *and* JOHN KNIGHT.)

MARTHA: Oh, it's you again.

PETER: It's Samuel we've come to see, if you please, Martha.

MARTHA: You know Samuel's mind so far as your business is concerned, Peter Saxton.

SAMUEL: Who is it, Martha?

MARTHA (*to* PETER): You do us no good by calling here. (*She makes to close the door.*)

SAMUEL: Let them in, Martha.

MARTHA (*turning towards* SAMUEL): It's Peter Saxton and his friends. Don't have any truck with them, Samuel.

SAMUEL (*rising and going towards the door*): That's no way to treat visitors, Martha. Come in the three of you. (*They enter and stand in the centre of the room.*)

JOHN: Good evening, Samuel.

SAMUEL: Evening, John. Don't see you at chapel these days. Are you so busy with saving the world that you have no time for saving your own soul?

JOHN (*ignoring his remark and walking up to the loom*): Didn't expect to find you with work on your hands, Samuel. Precious few of your neighbours have any.

SAMUEL: Aye, there's not too many orders these days. Sit you down and Martha will make us a mug of tea. Is there any tea, Martha?

MARTHA: Send them away, Samuel. You know what happens once they start their talk . . .

SAMUEL: That'll do, Martha. We're not so destitute we can't offer a little Christian hospitality. (*She hesitates.*) Martha, do as I ask. (MARTHA *walks to the stove.*) No there's not much work and for what there is the rates are lower than they've ever been. It's hard to make ends meet. (*Pause.*) It's about next Monday's meeting you've come, isn't it?

ROBERT: We know what you think of the Union, Samuel, and that you're against the remedies we propose.

MARTHA (*turning abruptly to face the men*): Aye, that we are! Burning factories, smashing machines . . .

PETER: You've no right to talk like that, Martha. We're against action of that sort and always have been.

MARTHA: Maybe you are but your lot were behind the strike last year and where did that get you? I've seen you and your followers drilling in the fields. You know where you'll get poor folk? Shipped off to Botany Bay or thrown into the New Bailey prison. What do you hope to gain with all your speeches and marching? You can't stop the machines and the factories! You're standing in the way of progress!

ROBERT (*with controlled intensity*): Progress do you call it, Martha? Just take a look out of this window. That was trees and grass out there less than ten year ago. A man could breathe God's air and see the sky. And now? After ten years of progress? Not a flower to be seen or a bird to be heard. Mile upon mile of black squalor and more of it stretching out as each day passes. (*Turning to face* SAMUEL.) And you, Samuel? What does Martha's progress mean to you? What did you earn last week?

SAMUEL: Eight shillings I earned last week and that were a good week.

ROBERT: And what were left out of that for maintenance?

SAMUEL: Two shillings and threepence. Mind you, Agnes brings home nine or ten shilling a week. I don't think we could manage without hers.

ROBERT: Things have come to a pretty pass when a craftsman's daughter makes more than he does. I can remember when you earned four times as much and so can you, Samuel.

SAMUEL: Aye, they were better days. I need no persuading of that.

JOHN: Where's the progress in things getting worse, Martha?

MARTHA (*angrily*): Hold your tongue, John Knight! And what do you have to offer us in our suffering? Meetings and more meetings! Petitions, marches, demonstrations. All stirred up by that loud-mouthed tub-thumper, Henry Hunt. That man will lead us all to hell and damnation!

SAMUEL: Mind your language, Martha. That's no way for a God-fearing woman to talk. Now that they've come I shall listen to what they have to say. (*He turns to face the men.*)

PETER: Next Monday's meeting will very likely be the biggest ever seen in Lancashire, in England I shouldn't wonder. Working people from twenty miles around will be marching to Manchester. Every brass band in the county will be out. It'll be a grand day, Samuel. A proud day. But solemn, too. On that day we shall be asserting our rights as men and women to live our lives in freedom and equality. So far the powers-that-be have ignored us. We're just a political minority without real support, they think. And that's why we want you to join us, Samuel. You're known to be a fair man with no axe to grind. With you, and men like you in our ranks, it will be clear to all the world that ours is a people's movement and a people's cause. Give us your support, Samuel.

SAMUEL: And what shall be the business of the meeting?

PETER: To consider how we may elect a member of Parliament to represent the people of Manchester at Westminster.

MARTHA: You must be mad! What have they at Westminster to do with the likes of us?

PETER: I'll tell you, Martha. Working people everywhere suffer but it's at Westminster you'll find the seat of the mischief. The Constitution's become rotten at the core – in Parliament itself. This is the source and the only source of all our sufferings. And what's the remedy? Reform! A Radical, complete constitutional reform! Give us a reformed Parliament so that it can guarantee every poor man work and good wages for doing it. That's how we shall better our lot!

SAMUEL: There's much in what he says, Martha. It's the Parliament that makes the laws and a lot of them are rank bad ones.

MARTHA: Samuel, I beg you not to go. I fear for us all.

SAMUEL: Why should you fear, Martha? No harm would come to us. It shall be a peaceful meeting, shan't it?

JOHN: So far as we have any say, it will. We want to show that we have no need of force, that we can gain our rights peaceably. The strength of our unity will overcome them. Join us, Samuel.

SAMUEL: You know why I've hesitated up to now, don't you? I've never held with making demands and threats. God didn't mean us to carry on like that. But I have my doubts, I must confess. God didn't mean us to tolerate cruelty and injustice either. That far I'm with you. But I shall need time to think and to pray for guidance. I shall let you know what I decide. And you, Martha, I shall need your help. (MARTHA *places a teapot upon the table.*)

PETER: Thank you, Martha. We'll not have time for tea.

PETER (*to* SAMUEL): Some of us will be up on Middleton field tomorrow evening for a marching practice. You'd be welcome.

ROBERT: Good-night, Samuel, Martha.

JOHN: Give our regards to Agnes, Martha. It's her future too we're making.

   (MARTHA *does not turn to face them.*)

SAMUEL (*shaking each of them by the hand*): Robert, John, Peter.

   (*They leave through the hall the way they came.* MARTHA *and* SAMUEL *face one another across the table. As* SAMUEL *returns to his loom his daughter,* AGNES, *makes her way through the hall. She walks slowly stopping occasionally to cough violently. She enters the kitchen, haggard and tired.*)

MARTHA: You're late tonight, lass, aren't you. Had a hard day at the mill? (*As she approaches.*) Bless me, what ails you, child? You're as white as a sheet.

AGNES: They've turned me away from the mill, Mother. I can't go back. They gave me half a day's pay and told me I was sacked.

SAMUEL: Sacked! Why in heaven's name?

AGNES: I'm no use to them, Father. I can't keep on my feet. I was so drowsy and shaky today I fell against the frame. The overseer kicked me and I fainted: when I came to I was shivering and sweating. He told me to get out. And now I've got this cough. It's the dust and the damp. I'm sorry, Father. I tried not to give in.

SAMUEL: Of course you did, lass. Just you come and sit in the chair and rest awhile. (*He helps her across to the armchair.*) Martha, get our Agnes some hot gruel. (*He wraps her in a shawl. She begins to cough falteringly.*) We'll take care of our Agnes.

AGNES: How shall we get by, Father? My wages were half of what we earned. But I feel so tired, Father. I know that if I go into another mill, it'll kill me. (*She begins to sob.*)

SAMUEL: There my little one. Don't fret.

AGNES: What are we to do, Father? What are we to do?

SAMUEL: Aye, that's the problem, child. (*Holding the girl's head against his side and glaring at* MARTHA.) What do you say, Martha? *You* tell us what we must do.

Lights fade. CURTAIN.

PART TWO

A street outside Kate's house. It is a warm August night, 1819. KATE *enters running followed quickly by* TOM. KATE *stops in the centre of the hall with her back to* TOM. *She is breathing vigorously.* TOM *stands a yard or two behind her. From the distance the strains of 'The Weavers' March' can be heard.*

KATE: I've run too much, Tom. I've no more breath. (*She bends her body to catch her breath.*) What with dancing all evening and rushing through the streets, I'm tired out, and no mistake. I should be getting in. Father will be wondering where I am.

TOM (*stepping round to face her*): You shan't go in till you give me your answer, Kate. You said you'd tell me before you bade me good-night. (*She lowers her head.*) Well, Kate?

KATE: Oh, Tom, how can we marry? You know that I'm fond of you . . .

TOM: Fond? It's more than that I feel for you, Kate. And more than that I hope you feel for me! (*He turns his head sulkily.*)

KATE: Look at me, Tom. (*Slowly he raises his eyes to meet hers.*) Have I ever as much as looked at another man since first I met you two year ago? Loving and courting's easy enough, Tom, but marrying's different. Haven't we worries enough as it is?

TOM: But if we were wed, Kate, the worries would be shared.

KATE: Not shared, Tom. Rather doubled. I've Father to look after and the children since Mother died. You know that it's on me they depend. Am I to start another family with only the same means to live on?

TOM: There'd be mine coming in. I might not be earning much at the present time but things are bound to get better.

KATE: How can you say that? Your own dad were a proud weaver a few years ago with wages enough to feed you all. Look at him now. Mostly idle; your mother out at work day and night and the kids hungry. You know what the winter will bring. Should we marry for the winter? Should marrying feed and clothe us?

TOM: You dwell too much on all that, Kate. We could go away from here – to Bolton or Leeds or Oldham. There's work in those parts and a man can earn a living wage.

KATE: For his wife and children too? Or shall they work all the hours God sends? I don't want our kids bent and broken in the mill, dead before they're full-grown. It's not right to bring young ones into such a world.

TOM: Then we shall change our world, Kate. Go somewhere else. Folk in these parts are too tied down. There's no future here for us. Marry me, Kate, and we shall start a new life together. (*Pause.*) Please, Kate.

KATE: You're a stubborn one you are, Tom. I've told you before and I tell you again, I shan't leave here so long as my dad's poorly and the kids need looking after. There's work enough in Manchester for women. But you're right. There is no future here – for you.

(TOM *turns and very slowly begins to walk away.*)
Tom! Come back, you daft thing! Tom!
(*But he goes on.* KATE *turns as if to make for the house.*)
Well, if that's it, I'll be bidding you good-night!

TOM (*turning and running back before she reaches the door*): Don't go in yet, Kate! I can't bear us to part when we've been cross. (*She pauses with her back to him.*) If I were to go, Kate, should you think of me and wait till I got back?

KATE: Are you so certain you'd come back?

TOM: I should come back, Kate.

KATE: Then I should wait for there's no one else I'm ever likely to care for. (*Pause.*) I have to be getting in, Tom. It's near enough eleven and you know what time the early shift begins.

TOM: I should send for you when I was settled and saved a bit.

KATE: Dad'll need putting to bed. He could hardly raise himself out of his chair this morning his breathing's so bad. Good-night, Tom.

TOM: Your dad could come too. He always says Manchester's too
 damp for his chest.

KATE: Aye, that's true. Good-night. I did like the dancing, Tom.
 (TOM *kisses her quickly on the forehead and then turns to go.*)

TOM: Good-night, Kate. (*She goes in and he leaves the hall.*)

PART THREE

The George Leigh Union Room, Manchester. A dozen members of the Manchester Female Reform Society are preparing flags, liberty caps and banners for the forthcoming meeting in Manchester. Above their heads is inscribed a huge placard which reads: WOMEN OF MANCHESTER! FOR LIBERTY AND EQUALITY!

ELIZABETH WALMSLEY *sits in a prominent position at the end of the hall facing the others who are spaced in front of her.*

JANE: How were the dance last night, Kate?

KATE: It were all right. (*She looks a little downcast.*)

DAISY: Something up between you and your Tom?

DOROTHY: I heard Tom were thinking of leaving Manchester. Going to Oldham to make his fortune.

KATE: He does talk of it.

EMILY: There's too much of this money chasing, if you ask me. Men leaving home and family for a shilling or two extra a week. You have to settle somewhere and wherever the men go they'll land up sooner or later against the masters – and a fat lot of good that'll do them.

KATE: There's precious little work for Tom in these parts. He says folk round here are too tied down and that a man must go after work if he wants to live a decent life.

ELIZABETH: The trouble with your Tom, Kate, is his bottom's still wet.

KATE: What's Manchester got to offer Tom?

ELIZABETH: Hasn't he learnt yet that you simply cannot run away from the masters? Your Tom is a little scab, if you ask me. Always after his own good and the devil take the rest.

KATE: You've no right in saying that, Mrs Walmsley. Tom only says . . .

ELIZABETH (*interrupting*): Tom only says that if things get too bad for you here then clear off somewhere else. And what of those who can't clear off?

EMILY: Some of our kids are already starving, Kate Farleigh, and nowhere for their fathers to go.

DAISY: Don't get on at her so. Wouldn't the most of us leave Manchester if we could? There's hardly a man in work and the price of food never stops going up. I've lost four of my little ones in the last two years. The doctor calls it consumption but what really eats them away is the want of nourishment. How can a little mite last out the winter on porridge and potatoes?

ELIZABETH: The masters will tell you to go on to Parish Relief – if you can get quarter of an hour from the mill to go and ask for it.

EMILY: And when you get it, *if* you get it, the masters straight away cut your wages on the grounds that you don't need so much to live on. They'll get you all ways.

ELIZABETH: And that's the reason for the meeting next Monday. The only answer to the masters is to stand together and, if we must, *fight* together.

JANE: Will that Mr Hunt from London be there?

ELIZABETH: He will.

JANE: He were at the January meeting, weren't he. He's a very fine talker is Mr Hunt.

JOANNA: And a fine one with the ladies too from all accounts! (*The women greet this with cries of mock alarm and shock.*)

JANE: Joanna Watson's a very proper young lady, aren't you? For myself I should welcome Mr Hunt's attentions. I should imagine him a very charming wooer!

JOANNA: Just listen to her!

JANE (*rising from her chair*): Delighted I'm sure, Mr Hunt. I can think of no greater pleasure than to join you in the dance. (*She dances around the hall towards the door, the women gaping. Near the extreme end of the hall she giggles and says:*)
Mr Hunt, how could you suggest such a thing!

(*At this moment the doors are thrown open and in walks Mrs Cranford who faces the transfixed Jane for a moment.*)

Good evening, Mrs Cranford. (*She runs to her seat.*)

MRS CRANFORD: Good evening to you all! Busily preparing for the meeting, I see.

(*A few of the women stand up awkwardly.*)

ELIZABETH: I wish some of you would get out of my light. I can't see to do my stitching. (*She stares at those standing who resume their seats.*)

EMILY: It's not often we see you down this end of the town, Mrs Cranford.

ELIZABETH: Quite the grand lady, our Mrs Cranford, since her husband started his own mill. We were near enough neighbours ten years ago, when George Cranford were a cottage weaver in Middleton.

MRS CRANFORD: God has been good to us, Elizabeth, that's true. But I trust I am not unmindful of the responsibilities which go with good fortune. Indeed it is out of recognition of your distress that I come to you today.

EMILY: What do your kind care about our distress? If the masters were to give the men a decent wage there'd be less distress for good ladies like yourself to worry over.

EMMA: Not all of us feel as Emily does, Mrs Cranford. Your husband were always a fair man. Not all the masters are devils, Emily. Won't you sit, Mrs Cranford? (*She offers her a chair.*)

MRS CRANFORD: Thank you, Emma. I shall stand since what I have to say must be brief.

DOROTHY: Don't give us any sermons about the virtues of patience and forbearance. We've heard enough on that subject, Mrs Cranford. You shall go home to roast beef and strawberries. We must make do with porridge and potatoes. It's work for our men and food for our kids we want.

JOANNA: We'll hear you Mrs Cranford.

MRS CRANFORD: Thank you, Joanna. As you all know I was

recently elected chairman of the Committee for the Relief of the
Distressed Poor and their Families . . .

ELIZABETH: Angel of Mercy!

MRS CRANFORD: The Committee have asked me to tell you that
they are prepared to set up a kitchen in these rooms for the daily
provision of nutritious soup to the poor and their families. To this
end and as a token of our goodwill (*looking at* ELIZABETH), even
towards those who regard us as enemies, I come to you to ask for
your co-operation in the distribution of the soup. We hope that
you will make our offer known among your friends, and neighbours so that all those in need shall benefit. (*She surveys the women
who remain unmoved.*) I trust that you will not refuse this kindness
which I assure you is offered in a spirit of Christian charity.

ELIZABETH: We shall consider your offer, Mrs Cranford. God
knows our young ones are hungry but there's a gulf between the
rich and the poor and it'll take more than a bowl of soup to close
it. We never received anything for nothing from the masters or
their wives. We shall have to judge the cost of accepting, for cost
there shall surely be.

MRS CRANFORD: As you please, Elizabeth. Your views are well
known to us all and even if we don't always agree . . .

ELIZABETH: Of course we don't. Our views, like our needs, are
different from yours. (*The two women regard each other a moment and
then* MRS CRANFORD *turns to go.*)

MRS CRANFORD: Let me know to what decision you come. I shall
call again in a day or two. And now, good-bye to you all.

(*She turns and walks away. She stops just short of the door.*)
I hope you will accept.

(*She leaves. The women slowly resume their sewing. No one speaks.
They are waiting for* ELIZABETH *to speak first. After a few tense
moments,* ELIZABETH *looks up from her work.*)

ELIZABETH: Well, what do we tell her? She'll want to know soon
enough and so will the newspapers, for you can be sure she hasn't
neglected to tell them of her Committee's offer.

(*As the following speeches are delivered the women rise from their seats until at the close of the scene all are on their feet. The women express their viewpoints with animation and feeling.* ELIZABETH *remains seated and immobile until she speaks at the end of the scene.*)

EMMA: Why were you so bitter against her, Elizabeth? There's many a mother round here longing to see their children fed – even on charity soup!

DAISY: I've seen too many of mine perish for the lack of food. Little Margaret has been thirteen hours in the mill today and what I'm to give her tonight when she gets home I don't know. She could do with the soup, poor little mite.

MAUREEN: It were because of the famine we left Ireland two years ago. It don't seem right to refuse food when it's offered.

EMMA: I'm for taking her soup.

DOROTHY: And I'm against and I'll tell you why. (*Looking at* ELIZABETH.) You formed this Society only a year ago. Things have not got any easier since and there's no saying they have – but what I've gained in a year is – well – pride. What galls is just waiting for the worst and lying down under it. So long as we are beholden to Mrs Cranford's charity, we shan't have the pride to stand up and demand what is rightfully ours.

JANE: I'm with Dorothy on that, Elizabeth.

FANNY: There's much in what you say, Dorothy. Not so long ago I should have thought the way you do. But times have changed me. Twelve months ago when Wakeford's locked out the men, we were reduced to seven shillings a week and eight mouths to feed. William hasn't worked since and it's telling on him.

EMILY: Kate's Tom would tell you to clear off to Oldham. Milk and honey there, you know.

FANNY: Shiftin's no use either. You know what became of us when we decided to make for Nottingham. Turned out of Buxton as vagrants, robbed of our savings and no redress. Tiny catches the fever and we bury her in Disley. You live or perish where you're born. I'd take the soup, Elizabeth.

EMMA: I'm for accepting. You know we're all behind the men in their struggle. We'll all be at the meeting on Monday but there's the present to think of as well as the future and the children need the soup.

JOANNA: Mrs Cranford made her offer in a spirit of Christian charity. Have we grown so hard that we cannot accept in a spirit of Christian humility?

EMILY: That's a lot of daft talk, that is. Where's your Radical spirit, woman! If we accept their soup where do we end up? Dependent on the masters for our rent and heat and on their wives for our daily food. Tell them we'll go without, I say.

ANNE: I'm with our Emily.

ELIZABETH (*dispassionately*): And you, Kate. Should we take Mrs Cranford's soup?

(KATE *does not answer at once. The others look at her expectantly.*)

KATE: I don't rightly know what to decide.

ELIZABETH: But decide you must. Want of decision will make you a slave, Kate – to the masters and to your Tom if you're not very careful.

KATE (*rising in anger*): Will you stop pestering me with talk of what Tom wants and doesn't want. I've told Tom that I shan't go with him to Oldham and it weren't easy, I can tell you. Let me be a moment.

ELIZABETH: I'm sorry for talking so harshly, Kate.

EMILY: We've all had a say, Elizabeth.

ELIZABETH (*standing*): And by my reckoning half are for accepting and half against. You know already how I feel but I shall have my say even so. Next Monday thousands of working people will gather on St Peter's Field to hear our great leaders. Everyone of them present at that meeting will be there for one simple reason in the end – they've suffered too much and they'll have that suffering ended. Not that it's been in vain, mind you. Every victory we have won, every gain made has come out of solidarity in the face of suffering. The masters combine to oppress us – we must combine to be free. But be warned! They will stop at nothing to discredit and disunite us. If we refuse their charity soup the papers will call us heartless for not relieving our children's misery. But who causes their misery? The masters! Let us tell them that what we want is not the crumbs from their tables but the means to feed and clothe our families. Mrs Cranford and her kind would distract us from our true purpose. Fellow women, it will not be easy but let us say *no* to the soup!

(EMILY, DOROTHY, JANE *and* ANNE *applaud. The others remain silent.*)

EMMA: And those of us against you, Elizabeth? What shall we do?

ELIZABETH: Go and tell your Mrs Cranford that you're ready to accept but she shan't set her kitchen up here. Joanna, go and give her your names on your way home.

JOANNA: Very well, Elizabeth. And you, Kate. Shall I give her your name along with ours?

KATE: No, we'll do without the soup. (JOANNA *leaves, slowly followed by the other women. Only* ELIZABETH *and* KATE *remain.*)

ELIZABETH (*placing her arm round* KATE's *shoulder and walking with her to the door*): Come round to ours, Kate. We'll find a morsel of something in the larder and I've a little tea we can brew.

(*They leave.*)

PART FOUR

A field near Middleton three days before the march to Manchester. A group of local men: farm-labourers, weavers, spinners, driers and printers enter in a disorderly and lackadaisical fashion. They are a sorry spectacle, unkempt but cheerful and talkative. They discuss the forthcoming march to Manchester. They stand about. Within seconds ROBERT DRUMMOND, *Secretary of the Salford Union Society enters. He shakes some of them by the hand. The men greet him warmly. They obviously admire and trust him. He ascends a high point in the midst of them.*

DRUMMOND: Welcome, Brothers!
   (*The men respond with cries of 'Welcome to you!; Good old Bob!' etc.*)
   Where's Jack Partridge? Not still ailing is he?
FIRST MAN: Jack passed away last night, Robert. (*The men remove their hats and lower their heads.*) We told the master the fumes in the dye-shop would kill him but they wouldn't shift him. He had a rotten chest, poor Jack.
DRUMMOND: John, see that his widow gets a contribution from the Union. It'll be precious little and her with six young 'uns to feed. (*A second or two's pause, and then looking around.*) And Fearless O'Connor and Michael McShea? Where are the Irishmen?
SECOND MAN: Slung into prison, Brother Robert. The magistrates charged them with organizing strikes.
DRUMMOND (*stands silent and angered for a moment*): It is for their sake that we meet today and march to Manchester on Monday. Not one of us is free until every man held in bondage has been released. (*He looks around again.*) No sign of Samuel Coppitt. Will he not join us?

KNIGHT: We called on him but he is not decided. Martha is against us.

DRUMMOND: We shall march without him if we must. Though God knows we need all the support we can get. We're used to the taunts that we're a rabble without unity or purpose. But the march to Manchester will shake them! Men, you know our cause is a just one! (*Cries of Hear! Hear!*) But do we do our cause justice? (*He gets down and walks among them, 'inspecting' them.*) Do we carry ourselves as if our cause were our inspiration? (*He shakes his head.*) Just look at you! The masters will quake just to see you. Listen brothers, when we march we must look as if we're ready to take charge of ourselves, ready to govern and govern well. Do you remember the Blanket march to London two years ago? We all set out with high intentions, didn't we? 'March on the capital! A hundred thousand before we get to Birmingham!' And what happened? Three hundred left Manchester and one man turned up in London! One man! How they jeered! But not this time, brothers! This time we'll show them we mean business. (*Bracing himself like a sergeant-major.*) Now men, into your drilling order! (*The men shuffle about confusedly. The 'line' should come out with the notably tall standing alongside the markedly short. This scene presents one of the few opportunities in the play for humour, though nothing should detract from the men's eventual resolve and seriousness.*) In the name of God what sort of line is that! No wonder they laugh! Roger Payne come here. (ROGER *is the tallest and the others take up their positions in order of declining height.*) That's better. Now let's have a good look at you. (*He observes that one of the men is holding a pike.*) John Prentice, put that pike away!

PRENTICE: I ain't going on any march without something to defend myself with. We went to St George's Field all peaceable and they cut us down like turnips with their sabres and swords. It's force they respect. (*One or two murmurs of assent.*)

DRUMMOND: So *they* might. *We* don't. If it comes to force they will win every time. Its the way of peace they don't understand. Put down your pike, John, or you don't take your place with us (PRENTICE *hesitates. The men regard him with concern. After a moment he puts aside his pike.*) Good man, John. Right men, back into line! Heads up! Left turn! Quick march!

(*Again there is confusion.*)

Is that how you would gain your liberties? What a hopeless lot you are!

THIRD MAN: It's years since we drilled. Not since the wars against the French and God knows we've reason enough to forget all that!

DRUMMOND: That was not your war, Peter! Then we fought for our masters. But this is *our* fight and we must fight it well! Our line must be straight, our heads held high, our marching regular. Once more! Attention!

(*At this moment* SAMUEL COPPITT *appears and stands waiting away from the line. It slowly occurs to the men that* SAMUEL *is there. They break line slightly to get a view of him.* JOHN KNIGHT *leaves the rank and confronts him.*)

KNIGHT: Good-day, Samuel. And will you join us?

SAMUEL: Aye, I will join you.

(*This is greeted with cheers and applause. The men gather round to shake his hand. He joins them in the rank.*)

DRUMMOND: Welcome, Samuel! Your coming has made our resolve the stronger. Right, back into line! Now take good note of your left and your right! Left turn! Quick march! (*The men march well.*) Left, right! Left, right!

(*He drills them continuously for a few moments. As they march he shouts encouragement to become even smarter. By stages their marching becomes excellent.*)

DRUMMOND: Halt! Now that's more like it. Well done! Dismiss!

(*The men break line and* DRUMMOND *ascends his raised platform.*)

Robert, will you collect his week's subscriptions?

ROBERT: How much this week, Brother?

DRUMMOND: As usual, a penny from every man in work. (*He*

begins to collect.) How many of you are in full-time work? (*Half raise their hands.*) And our masters tell us to be patient! Make the announcement please, Brother John. (JOHN *ascends the platform.*)

JOHN: Next week's Union meeting will take place at the George Street Rooms. Brother Johnston from Oldham will address us. The classes in political education will continue under the Reverend Joseph Harrison at the Mill Street Chapel. The Middleton contingent for next Monday's march will assemble here at seven in the morning. Last band practice tomorrow. (*He gets down.*)

DRUMMOND: Thank you, Brother. Our last business is to hear the contents of the Petition we propose to place before the Regent in London. (*As he ascends the platform to read the Petition, the men gather in front of him.*) We, the inhabitants of Manchester, and its vicinity, in our name and on behalf of our oppressed fellow-countrymen beg leave to approach your Royal Highness with a declaration of our grievances. (*Murmurs of Hear! Hear!*) First, we abhor the folly and pride shown by your Ministers who have led us into a series of expensive wars on the Continent. Second, we protest that these same Ministers have treated the people with every insult and indignity. They have ignored our pleas and suffered us to experience every species of distress and calamity. They have fettered and imprisoned in solitary dungeons some of the best and most worthy Englishmen. (*Further murmurs of Hear! Hear! and some applause.*) They have employed vile spies and informers and continually suspended the ancient laws of the land for the purpose of stifling the voice of the people. We beg to remind Your Highness that wherever rebellion has prevailed it has arisen not because of the people's love of violence but as a result of their hatred of oppression.

Should we be asked what it is we want, the answer is clear. (*Each if these demands is met with loud and enthusiastic cheering. Indeed this whole speech requires the animated participation of the men if it is to really come to life.*) A change of government! An end to corruption! A reformed Parliament! The repeal of the accursed

Corn Laws! The right of all men and women to make their own laws and to reap the fruits of their own toil! That's it men! (*They cheer lustily.*) Who's for it! (*An even louder cheer.*)

Right men! Into line! (*They form up smartly.*) By the left quick march! Left, right! Left, right!

(*The file marches twice or so around the hall. As they march, the sound of marching music arises. On their last circuit before leaving the hall the volume grows louder. They leave shouting the familiar slogans:* 'WE WANT THE VOTE!': 'DOWN WITH THE CORN LAWS!': 'SET THE PRISONERS FREE!')

(*Lights fade. One spot picks out* DEAN *who remains. He runs towards the stage. The curtains open to reveal the* MAGISTRATES *waiting impatiently at the Bull Inn.*)

PART FIVE

The Bull Inn, Manchester. Late evening. As DEAN *proceeds towards the stage the magistrates exhibit their restlessness.* NORRIS, *the Manchester Stipendiary Magistrate, paces the room.* WILLIAM HULTON, *the Chairman of the Magistrates, sits at a table which he nervously taps with his fingers.* HUGH BIRLEY, *Second in Command, the Manchester Yeomanry, stands looking into the fireplace.* JOHN MOORE, *the First Constable, stands to one side.* JOSEPH NADIN, *the Permanent Deputy Constable, is reading documents from a case. Only* GENERAL BYNG *remains calm and immobile.* DEAN's *loud knock at the door galvanizes the group into alert attentiveness.*

NORRIS (*moving towards the door*): Who's there?

DEAN: 'Tis I, Sire. Dean!

(NORRIS *opens the door, takes a few paces towards centre. All eye him intently, anxious to learn his news.*)

NORRIS: Well?

DEAN (*breathing heavily*): A moment, if you please, Your Worships. I've just run from Middleton Fields and it's a tidy distance.

NORRIS: Make haste, man. What have you to report?

DEAN: Ugly plans are afoot, Your Worships. The county is rife with unrest and sedition.

NADIN: Sedition? What kind of sedition?

DEAN: Organized sedition, Mr Nadin. I've never seen so much drilling and marching.

NADIN: They don't suspect who you are, Dean?

DEAN: Oh no, Your Worships. They regard me as one of their friends.

NORRIS: And what did you observe at Middleton?

DEAN: Signs of trouble, Sires. Drummond inflames them with demands for reform, minimum wages and the repeal of the Corn

Laws. I can assure you there will be tens of thousands at Manchester on Monday and all of them insistent that their claims be satisfied.

MOORE (*apprehensively*): Were any of them armed, Dean?

DEAN: Aye, with picks and staffs.

MOORE: Had any of them firearms?

DEAN: I know not, Sire, but they are all possessed of a terrible vengeance. They call the coming meeting, the day of reckoning.

NORRIS: Aye, it will be that all right. We have wavered too long. Now is the time for decisive action. Anything further to report, Dean?

DEAN: Nothing to report, Your Worship, but a request if I may . . .

NORRIS: Well, what is it?

DEAN: Times are very bad, as you know, Your Worships, and as a poor man has many mouths to feed . . .

NORRIS: Come now, Dean, if we pay you too well you'll get fat and prosperous and your Radical friends will suspect you are in the pay of the magistrates. You know what your fate would be then, don't you, Dean? (*He makes a throat-cutting gesture.*) Now be off with you and keep your wits about you.

DEAN: Very good, Your Worship. Good-day to you all, Sires. Good-day. (*He bows out obsequiously.*)

BYNG: Contemptible wretch! How can you have dealings with such a man? His kind has too much interest in creating mischief even when it doesn't exist.

MOORE: Come, General, you are too particular. In times such as these we must take help from whatever quarter it is offered. To be forewarned is to be forearmed. Surely as a soldier you appreciate that.

BYNG: I am opposed to the use of spies and informers. Most of them are proven liars and on more than one occasion their so-called information has been exposed in the courts as fabrication. What trust in the authorities can the people have when every one of them walks in fear of government agents? There will soon be less liberty in England than in Russia.

BIRLEY: In Russia, General, any Jacobin who so much as opens his mouth is packed off to Siberia. Wouldn't mind seeing a few of ours packed off with 'em.

NADIN: You were always a man for action, eh Mr Birley?

HULTON: The General is right to fear the loss of liberty and few of us, I am sure, would wish to see it reduced further.

MOORE: But consider our situation, General. Manchester grows at a fantastic rate. It is, I believe, seven or eight times larger than when I was a boy. Few of those living in the town were born here. Irish immigrants, impoverished farm-workers, men from all over the country are flooding into the town. And what means of control do we have? A few constables!

BIRLEY: There is the Manchester Yeomanry, of course.

MOORE: Quite so, but you and your companions are not full-time law officers, are you?

BIRLEY: Ah, but we know how to deal with these infernal Jacobins. You can depend on us to put 'em down.

NADIN: You put them down at St George's and no mistake, eh Mr Birley?

MOORE: Let us not forget either the temper of the times. For many months we have suffered the terrors of siege; Manchester is surrounded by armies of restless reformers and agitators. I do assure you, gentlemen, that as I retire at night I am always fearful that our town will be in flames by morning. Few of you live in Manchester; those of us who do are very near desperate.

NORRIS: Mr Moore is right. We are sitting on a powder keg. Nadin, how many do you reckon will be attending the meeting?

NADIN: Hard to say, but detachments are certainly coming from fifty towns and villages around. Well over fifty thousands I would say. Maybe more.

MOORE: Tell me, Deputy Constable, shall women and children be at the meeting?

NADIN: In large numbers, so I am informed.

MOORE: And what do you make of that?

NADIN: I fear, Your Worships, that the women and children are a shield behind which the plotters may seek to conceal their plans. I am certain that we should put down this demonstration, if necessary in the harshest manner.

BIRLEY: I'm with you there, Nadin. We shall put 'em down. Just give us the chance. Speaking for the Yeomanry many of us think you've let too much pass already. Some of these Jacobins have no respect, you know. Firmness is what they understand.

HULTON: We shall undoubtedly have to be prepared to take rapid and decisive action. Mr Nadin, will the constables and the Yeomanry be sufficient to manage an assembly of this size?

NADIN: Not if there's the slightest suspicion of trouble. I am of the opinion that a detachment of regular cavalrymen should be held in readiness.

BYNG: To be employed only in the event of the most extreme provocation, of course.

NORRIS (*pointedly*): To be employed as we feel the situation warrants, General.

BYNG: Have I understood you aright? If troops are to be used they will presumably be under my command.

NORRIS: Under *our* command, General. In cases of civil unrest the magistrates alone are responsible for the restoration of order.

BYNG: But this is monstrous! I cannot possibly agree to such a plan. I was in sole command during the Cotton strikes and the Blanket March two years ago. In neither case was it necessary to do more than threaten force and peace was restored. Am I to risk the possibility of my men being used against the civil population and to have no say in how and when they shall be used?

NORRIS: Extreme dangers require extreme remedies, General. If, of course, you are not satisfied with our intentions then you are free to take whatever action you may consider necessary to dissociate yourself from us.

BYNG: And that is precisely what I shall do, Norris. But before I go I wish to register my deep concern as to the course you are adopting. These reformers are not criminals or insurgents. Many of them are honest to goodness working folk with genuine grievances. I've had dealing with them. Treat them in a civilized fashion and you will get much further.

NORRIS: Is that all, General?

BYNG: Not quite. Many of my finest troops are the sons and husbands of some who will be at Manchester. Proceed with caution, gentlemen. Lose the support of the troops and there'll be nothing between you and insurrection. I urge you most strongly to act with restraint. Goodnight to you all. (*He leaves.*)

NORRIS: I had anticipated the General would not see eye to eye with us. A pity, but unavoidable. Nadin, have you given the troops their orders?

NADIN: The 15th King's Hussars will be in place at the Wood Yard near St Peter's Square. At the first sign of trouble they will be summoned.

NORRIS: Suitably armed, of course.

NADIN: With swords. They are sharpening them now.

(*At this point the stage lights fade and the magistrates either 'freeze' for the duration of the soldier's soliloquy, or the curtains may be drawn and the scene resumed at the end of the soldier's piece.*

The SOLDIER, *a private cavalryman in the 15th King's Hussars, seats himself in the centre of the hall and talks to the audience in very conversational tones. He may well have a London accent. He should be ready to begin talking as soon as* NADIN *utters 'They are sharpening them now'.*)

SOLDIERS (*honing and feeling the blade*): Lovely! You could split a hair with it! Still, I never thought to use one of these again. Tell you the last time I used this. Battle of Waterloo! 'Gainst the Frenchies! That was a do that was. Wellington thought it was the greatest battle of the century. Unfortunately I wasn't there for the actual victory. Saw all the fighting before, mind you – but not the actual victory. No, as a matter of fact, two days before it was all over I got struck down by a French Lancer. Want to see the scar? (*He opens his tunic to reveal a scar up on his chest towards the shoulder. He turns in all directions so that they can all see.*) Happened at a place called Quatre Bras (*mispronounced quarter brass*). It was my own fault really. Should have seen it coming. I was out for five days. Three inches lower and I'd have been six feet deeper. (*He points to the ground.*)

Tell you how it happened. Just before I got this (*points to his wound*) I suddenly finds myself up close against this Frenchie on a damn great charger. Right out of the blue he came at me. I was so close to him I could feel my leg between the hot flank on his horse and mine. Well, he was too near to have a go at me, so he backs away a little. I could see right up his horse's nostrils – blown open they were like hunting horns, and foam dripping from his mouth. Real terror in his eyes, you know. And the poor blighter on his back! Screaming and hollering! All in French, mind you. He was hysterical. Cutting the air with his sabre, spurring his poor horse like mad. Well, he was a gift. Soon as he came at me I wheeled fast and got him from behind. (*He demonstrates with a heavy downwards thrust of his sword which he holds with both hands.*) He didn't stand a chance. I split him from shoulder to seat and he fell two sides of his horse. Then just as I was admiring my handiwork, up comes this Lancer, and smack! I was out for five days.

Mind you, I'd had enough by then. Some of my mates and me were ready to chuck it I can tell you. Would have done except for the Iron Duke. He was always up with the fighting, you know. Never hung back. (*He mounts his stool and holding his sword aloft imitates the emphatic manner of his supreme commander.*) 'There my lads, in with you. Give 'em what for, lads! At 'em, lads!' Yes, they had to rouse us. (*Descending.*) All that stinking mud. Well, that was war. (*He goes on sharpening his sword.*) We're all off to some meeting on Monday. Week-end leave's been cancelled. Order to prepare for special duty. Don't like these civil jobs. Mind you, there's no one else can do it. Them constables are useless, and as for the Yeomanry! Saw them in action a while back! Well, you never saw anything like it. Butchers and publicans most of them. Not a real horseman among them. Not a real horse neither, really. Well, I mean, those great draught horses! They weigh half a ton. They're no good in crowds.

Mind you, I've nothing against these Reformer fellers. Some of them a bit loud-mouthed, but they're all right. They reckon there'll be upwards of seventy thousand there. Lot of people on that bit of ground. Hope to God there's no panic. That's when the harm's done. Well, we shall see. You get your orders, don't you? Orders are clean-cut I say. That's why I enlisted in the first place. You know where you stand in the army. (*He continues to sharpen his sword. Spot fades. Resume to the Bull Inn.*)

(*The magistrates are now seated around a table with* HULTON *in a central position.*)

HULTON: Time is running out, gentlemen. We must quickly decide our course. Naturally much will depend on the support we receive from London. Nadin, what does the latest dispatch from the Home Office have to say?

NADIN (*takes a document from his case, undoes the ribbon and searches for the relevant passage*): Yes, here we are – 'Lord Sidmouth is of the opinion that the forthcoming meeting in Manchester should not be dispersed unless there is clear evidence that those in attendance intend to steal or riot' – That seems to be the relevant sentence.

BIRLEY: Why wait for things to get to such a pitch before acting, I say. If we wait until the speechifying begins there'll be no holding 'em. We should break it up before it even gets started.

HULTON: We must be careful not to exceed our legal powers, Mr Birley.

MOORE: Surely, Mr Hulton, *we* are the legal powers so far as Manchester's affairs are concerned. I must say the Home Secretary seems to have very little understanding of our situation. There he sits in London with a modern police force and troops thick upon the ground and he advises *us* to act with restraint. I don't find his advice at all encouraging.

NORRIS: And nor you should, Mr Moore. As the only full-time paid magistrate among you, it is my misfortune to have hosts of these Reformers and agitators brought up before me. During the last two years I have committed hundreds of them to prison but far from their support diminishing it daily gathers strength. I am in favour of a decisive blow on the grand scale. After all, it is they who have chosen to call it the Day of Reckoning.

(*There is a loud knock at the door. A* MESSENGER *holds a newspaper in his hand which he delivers to* NADIN.)

MESSENGER: The *Observer* has just arrived, Your Worships. Harrison's speech is on the front page.

NADIN: Thank you. (*The* MESSENGER *leaves.*) Shall I read the relevant passages, Mr Chairman?

HULTON: Yes, do.

NADIN (*reading*): 'The Reverend Joseph Harrison, friend of the poor and a prominent Radical leader last night declared at a meeting in Bolton: The people of England have a right to approach the throne with their complaints, but the avenues have been stopped by the very men who have a vested interest in screening their misdeeds from public investigation – this is a barrier of corruption and the people MUST BLOW IT UP OR BLOW IT DOWN.'

MOORE: If that is not a direct invitation to revolution then I for one do not understand the English language.

HULTON: Harrison may have, of course, been talking metaphorically...

NORRIS: Really, Mr Chairman, you astonish me. That sort of inflammatory talk is commonplace these days. Harrison himself took part in the storming of the Paris Bastille. He's a veteran revolutionary. Are we to stand idly by until, like the Bourbons, we are led one by one to the guillotine?

MOORE: Norris is right, Mr Chairman.

BIRLEY: That he is! Who are these wretches to threaten us? Men without name, office or property. Give 'em an inch today and they'll certainly be demanding a yard tomorrow. Leave 'em to us. We'll put 'em down. (*He spreads himself.*)

HULTON: Naturally gentlemen, I am anxious to abide by what you consider best ...

NORRIS: Excellent, Mr Chairman. Then this is what I propose. Early on Monday morning we should meet in the upstairs room of Mr Baxter's house which commands an excellent view of St Peter's Fields. Nadin, how many constables do you have?

NADIN: Two hundred all told.

NORRIS: Two hundred, eh. Well, it might be enough. I suggest we line them up on either side of a long gangway between Baxter's house where we shall be installed and the rostrum from where Hunt and his gang will be talking. At the first suspicion of anything irregular, we should command the Manchester and Cheshire Yeomanry to advance towards the rostrum and arrest the lot of them.

BIRLEY: You can depend upon us. We'll see to 'em.

NORRIS: If by chance the Yeomanry are prevented from carrying out their mission we shall then avail ourselves of the 15th King's Hussars who, no doubt, will disperse the entire assembly without delay. How does that strike you, gentlemen?

BIRLEY: A good plan, I say.

MOORE: Admirable, Norris. With three prongs of attack we shall surely keep matters under control. Manchester will show the country how to deal with these Reformers.

NORRIS: And you, Mr Chairman?

HULTON: What exactly did you mean by 'at the first sign of anything irregular'? A lot hangs on that phrase it seems to me ...

NORRIS: A good point, Mr Chairman. However, Nadin and I will know when trouble's brewing. We've seen enough of these demonstrations, eh, Nadin?

NADIN: Aye, that we have. And broken a few of 'em up too. We shall know the signs, Mr Chairman.

HULTON: Well, if you're absolutely sure ...

NORRIS: Absolutely, Mr Chairman.

HULTON: Then it only remains for me to declare this meeting over. We shall meet again on Monday at the house of Mr Baxter. Till then, gentlemen, may we all sleep soundly in our beds. (*He rises to leave.*)

BIRLEY: I shall sleep a lot more soundly *after* Monday, I can tell you. Good-night all! (*He and* HULTON *leave*).

MOORE: They can talk about sleeping soundly in their beds when they both live twenty miles from here. It's we who live in the middle of it they should worry about. Well, good-night. (*He leaves*).

NORRIS: Quite an evening, eh Nadin? With Byng out of the way and Hulton shall I say 'neutralized', events should prove decisive on Monday next.

NADIN: You handled them very well, if I may say so.

NORRIS: You may. (*Gathering his coat and hat.*) Well, I shall be getting along too.

NADIN: Before you go, what shall I communicate to Sidmouth? He has asked for a brief report on what we propose.

NORRIS (*turning at the door*): Tell him the magistrates of Manchester, having considered his advice, for which we tender our thanks, have decided at long last to take the necessary measures to rid Manchester, Lancashire and England of the mounting and terrible threat of revolution. Tell him that the time has come for a show of strength and that we intend to acquit ourselves accordingly. (*He puts on his hat.*) Good-night, Nadin. See you on Monday.

NADIN: Good-night, Mr Norris. (*He takes out pen and paper and begins to write, speaking the words aloud:*)

My Right Honourable and Most Esteemed Lord . . .

CURTAIN

PART SIX

St Peter's Fields, Manchester. Early afternoon, Monday, August 16th, 1819. This scene represents the climax of the play. It must above all other scenes carry real conviction and feeling. Much of its poignancy will depend upon the sharp contrasting of the early optimism and even cheerfulness of the crowd and the later desolation and grief which overtakes them. At a number of points the crowd is asked to 'freeze'. This denotes instantaneous stillness, like stopping a film.

The massacre is described by a reporter on the Manchester Courier *who is already in position at the entrance to the hall as the scene opens. The curtain having closed on the magistrates, a very rapid change of scene is now required. The* REPORTER's *opening remarks will give the opportunity for the change to take place. The curtains will open to reveal a movable rostrum bedecked with slogans and flags. (If producers would prefer to stage this entire scene at 'floor level' then the stage can meanwhile be set for the final scene in Samuel's house.) After a few moments of silence the* REPORTER *speaks:*

REPORTER: I am a reporter on the *Manchester Courier* and was assigned the task of reporting the events which occurred here on August 16, 1819. (*Holding up a notebook.*) This is the actual account written by me of those events as I witnessed them. (*He begins to read.*) I visited St Peter's Fields at exactly eleven o'clock. It was a warm day and the sun shone from out of a clear blue sky. (*A distant clock chimes the hour. He walks towards the stage. The curtains opens to show the rostrum. He mounts a low platform.*) A few moments after my arrival at the Field my attention was particularly attracted by a crowd of people advancing towards the ground. It included a number of boys, women and even small children. They marched in an orderly fashion and far from displaying signs of unrest or violence they seemed almost in a festive spirit.

(*During his last sentence the first distant strains of marching, singing and shouting are heard. The farther the distance from which they come the better the effect, though the delay before their actual appearance in the hall should not be too long. When the procession eventually enters the hall it should march and counter-march for a full two minutes. If this is imaginatively arranged, the illusion will be created that literally hundreds of actors are taking part. Many of them carry banners bearing slogans such as* ANNUAL PARLIAMENTS, ONE MAN ONE VOTE, DOWN WITH THE CORN LAWS, SET THE PRISONERS FREE, MANCHESTER DEMANDS REPRE-SENTATION, *etc. At a given cue, say a point in the music or a clash of cymbals, the* CROWD *freezes. This must not be ragged. The more abruptly the hubbub ends, the more effective the silence which follows.*)

REPORTER: This was a most peaceable assembly. There were neither swords nor muskets and but very few sticks . . .

OLD MAN: I carry a stick (*he holds it up in the air*), but I don't mean to harm nobody. I just can't keep up with the young 'uns without it.

(*The* CROWD *laughs and continues its marching for a few moments. During this phase those carrying banners and flags will probably need to be relieved of them. Later in the scene there will be a certain amount of inevitable scurry. It is important that no dangerous objects should be in use at this time.*

When the banners and flags have been removed the CROWD *takes up its 'meeting position' arranged in front of the rostrum. The* CROWD *should be well spaced and well back from the stage. They should not bunch between the audience and the rostrum.*

On a near-by balcony stand NORRIS, NADIN, HULTON *and* MOORE. *They must have a commanding view of the meeting and be well seen by the audience. Once in position the* CROWD *freezes.*)

MOORE: What an assembly! There must be sixty or seventy thousand of them. And they march like soldiers.

NORRIS: Exactly! Like soldiers! And what are soldiers for?

HULTON: They seem peaceable enough, however, No sign of arms anywhere. (*He surveys the field.*)

NADIN: I don't like the look of it! There are far more than we expected. Once this lot is let loose there'll be no holding them.

NORRIS: Your constables in position, Nadin?

NADIN: As ordered. Mr Birley and the Yeomanry are stationed to the right of us down there. (*He points and calls.*) At the ready, Mr Birley?

BIRLEY (*his voice only from some distance*): Aye! At the ready! (*The Yeomanry are as yet out of sight.*)

REPORTER: By now the multitude was numerous. I made my way to the outskirts of the crowd and got upon a wall from which I obtained a good view of the entire scene.

(*He climbs upon a wall and surveys the* CROWD.)

I do not think there could have been less than seventy thousand persons present. It was in truth a most impressive assembly. A breathless expectation seemed now to pervade the multitude, when suddenly a distant drum was heard (*sound of drum*) and on to the field, accompanied by his party strode Mr Henry Hunt.

(*Enter* HUNT *and the company of* LEADERS *from the back of the hall. Band music plays.* HUNT *wears a white top-hat. He is a tall imposing figure. He smiles and waves. The* CROWD *does not move but one word goes through them and is repeated with mounting excitement:* '*Hunt!*' '*Hunt!*' *Hunt!' until his name echoes through the hall. Then some of the* CROWD *move towards him. He shakes them by the hands. He lifts up a child and then returns him to his mother. After a few moments he makes his way to the rostrum. He moves slowly and with great dignity. The* CROWD *applaud. As he reaches the front some of the men lift him on to their shoulders and carry him to the rostrum. As soon as he mounts the platform and raises his arm in greeting for the first time, the* CROWD *freezes.*)

NORRIS: Hunt has arrived! Just listen to that cheering!

HULTON: They certainly hold him in very great affection.

NADIN: Hunt has that crowd under his thumb. They'd do anything he commands. I don't like it.

MOORE: Listen! He's about to speak.

(*Renewed applause which dies as* HUNT *raises his hand for silence. He looks at the now silent and expectant crowd. The first words he utters should be almost inaudible.*)

HUNT: My friends, today is a great occasion . . .

CROWD: Speak up! Can't hear. Louder!

HUNT (*turning to his aides*): They can't hear me. The wind is in my face. Move the platform forward a few paces.

(*Four Radicals move the platform to the front of the stage.* HUNT *re-ascends it and another great cheer goes up. As he waves the* CROWD *freezes.*)

NORRIS: My God! They're moving the platform from the end of our gangway.

NADIN: They must have got wind of our plans!

NORRIS: This is a calculated attempt to evade arrest. Nadin, order the Yeomanry to arrest the men on the platform.

HULTON: Is that really necessary?

NORRIS: Really, Hulton, do you intend to let matters get out of hand before acting?

NADIN (*shouting in the direction of the Yeomanry*): Mr Birley! You are to arrest Hunt and his party forthwith!

HULTON: I must insist that before the Yeomanry disperse this assembly, the Riot Act is read in the prescribed manner.

NORRIS: As you wish, Mr Chairman. (*He takes out a long sheet of paper from which he prepares to read.*)

(HUNT *re-ascends the platform*)

HUNT: That's better! Can you hear me now?

CROWD: Yes!

HUNT: Today is a great landmark in the history of the Lancashire working class. We are gathered here to voice our legitimate protests against those who would deny us the right to work, the right to eat and above all, the right to vote. (*Loud cheers.*)

HUNT: But let me say, with all solemnity, that however just our demands there will be no disturbance of the peace. This meeting will be conducted in a peaceful and tranquil manner. I entreat each one of you, in the name of the cause we hold dear, to comport yourselves with restraint and civility. (*Further subdued applause and murmurs of assent.*)

(*During the following exchange between* NORRIS *and* HULTON *it is most important that the* CROWD *give no indication of hearing any word uttered from the balcony. The effect of not hearing can be created by skilfully interspersing the exchange with murmurings aside from the* CROWD. *The exchange should also be completed with rapidity.*

NORRIS (*reading with clarity but not loudly*): 'Our Sovereign Lord the King chargeth and commandeth . . .'

HULTON (*interrupting him*): But they can't hear a word you're saying, Norris. You'll have to read it from the platform.

NORRIS: Don't be a fool! Do you expect me to risk my life in the midst of that mob? (*He goes on.*) '. . . chargeth and commandeth all persons here assembled to disperse themselves.'

HULTON (*passionately*): But what's the use of that? They can't hear you, Norris!

NORRIS: But I'm reading it, aren't I, Mr Chairman? 'To disperse themselves and peaceably to depart upon Pain of Death. God Save the King!' There, Mr Chairman! The law has been observed.

HULTON (*with feeling*): Abused, Norris, not observed.

HUNT: This great meeting was originally called for last week, but as you know the authorities forbade us to gather. (*Murmurs of disapproval.*) They warned us that such an assembly would be illegal and that it would be broken up by force. (*Groans.*) Nevertheless, my friends (*raising his hand triumphantly*), here we are! (*Loud cheers.*) Not electing a member of Parliament – since that would be illegal! (*Laughter. As the laughter dies* HUNT *turns his gaze in the direction of the Yeomanry who are lined up in readiness.*) Are those the Yeomanry I see yonder?

(*The* CROWD *turns to look. Lights pick out a small group of Yeomen, each carrying a sabre. The Yeomen should be slightly raised and as far back as possible. Their expression should be menacing.*)

A VOICE: Aye, Mr Hunt. It's the Yeomanry!

(*The word 'Yeomanry' is taken up by the* CROWD. *There are murmurs of apprehension from among them.*)

HUNT: Do not be troubled. Have no fear. No doubt the magistrates have sent them to protect us! (*Laughter.*) We have no quarrel with the Yeomanry.

A VOICE: Let's give 'em a cheer! (*Murmurs of assent.*)

HUNT: An excellent idea! Three cheers for the Yeomanry! (*The* CROWD *give three hearty cheers. The Yeomanry cheer back though with vicious irony in their voices.*

Now the small group of Yeomanry begin to make their way through the crowd with bullying shouts of 'Make way! Stand back there!' The CROWD *make way for them without protest, though they close behind them as the Yeomanry reach the platform.* BIRLEY *stands squarely in front of the platform*).

BIRLEY: I have presently received instructions from the magistrates of this town to effect the arrest of you and your companions. I arrest you and order you to accompany me from this place.

HUNT: But this is monstrous! On what charge do you seek to arrest us? (*Murmurs from the* CROWD.) Where is your warrant? (*Further murmurs.*) Have the laws of England become so abused that a man can be apprehended without so much as a charge or a warrant? I shall not go with you. (*He turns away from them. The* CROWD *applauds.*)

BIRLEY: You refuse to accompany us?

HUNT: Aye, until you produce a proper warrant.

BIRLEY: Very well. (*The Yeomen turn towards the magistrates' window.* BIRLEY *signals to them and shouts*: Hunt and his party refuse to accompany us!

(*The* CROWD *become increasingly agitated and jostle the Yeomen whose way is blocked. They begin to brandish their sabres.*)

NORRIS (*loudly*): The Yeomanry are surrounded! Send in the Cavalry! Disperse this assembly at once!

(*Now the Yeomanry begin to threaten the* CROWD *with their sabres, but the* CROWD *does not disperse. There are cries of 'Help!' and one woman screams. At the same time a loud bugle blast is heard and from the back of the hall the Cavalry appear. For a few electric seconds everyone, including the Yeomen, freeze.*)

A VOICE: The soldiers have come!

ANOTHER: God save us all!

ANOTHER: They are moving towards us!

(*As these and other voices are heard the sound of horses' hooves is heard, at first quite softly and then with mounting thunderousness. As the pounding increases the* CROWD *wail and scream with terror.* HUNT *and his followers attempt to pacify the crowd with cries of 'Stand firm!'; 'Stand firm!' None of them as yet have fled from the ground.*

Now the troops enter the CROWD, *their swords slashing and cutting the helpless victims. Many fall to the ground. There are cries of pain from the wounded.*

After a short period of confusion those who are able flee from the hall, screaming as they go. Only the dead and wounded remain. Some attempt to hobble from the scene. Others cry pathetically for help. The Yeomen and the Cavalrymen wander among the bodies.

The MAGISTRATES *prepare now to leave the balcony from which they have witnessed the massacre.*)

MOORE: This'll put a stop to their demonstrations and meetings for a time eh, Nadin?

NADIN: Especially if we lock up the ringleaders!

NORRIS: We had no alternative! The Yeomanry were surrounded. We had to save 'em Mr Chairman.

HULTON (*with bitter irony*): We had to save them! But *who* will save *us*? (*He leaves.*)

(*As the Cavalrymen leave,* BIRLEY *and his fellow-Yeomen move towards* HUNT *and his party. They lead them away. As they make their way through the bodies,* HUNT, *overcome with grief, cries out:*)

HUNT: You wicked men! How could you! Innocent women and children! Oh, my God! My God! (*These cries continue until* HUNT'*s voice can no longer be heard. As the other prisoners are led away,* SAMUEL COPPITT, *who lies wounded, in the very centre of the hall, holds out a hand to* JOHN KNIGHT.)

SAMUEL: Brother John! Brother John! Here I am!

(BIRLEY *goes up to* SAMUEL *and strikes him with his sabre.* SAMUEL *falls to the ground.*)

KNIGHT: Samuel! Samuel! (*He attempts to go to him but he is dragged away. They leave. Only the casualties remain.*)

REPORTER: Now was a fit moment to effect my own escape. (*He descends the wall and makes his way across the hall describing the scene as he moves.*) I ran at first, scarcely knowing what to do. (*He runs falteringly among the bodies.*) On every side lay victims of the assault. (*He moves towards the exit.*) Never in my life had I witnessed such merciless cruelty. It was a terrible, terrible day. (*He leaves.*)

(*Lights fade to a reddish glow over the entire scene. The opening strains of* Shostakovitch's Eleventh Symphony *are an ideal musical 'support' to the action at this point. For a few seconds no one comes to the aid of those suffering, then slowly from the sides and entrances members of the crowd return to reclaim their loved ones. The women weep and cry out loudly. Some are distraught. Slowly and laboriously the wounded are helped to their feet, the dead lifted on to stretchers. The deserted field is scattered with articles of clothing and personal belongings. Only* SAMUEL COPPITT *remains – dead. A spot alights on his body. Four of his comrades, including* DRUMMOND, *enter and stand over him. They remove their hats. After a few seconds they lift* SAMUEL *on to their shoulders, his head thrown back. They are taking him home and their march should be 'routed' so that the audience have good time to witness* SAMUEL'*s solemn passage. As the cortège moves towards the stage the curtains are drawn to reveal Samuel's room with* MARTHA *waiting.*

The volume of the music may be slightly raised as the cortège mounts the stage.)

PART SEVEN

The kitchen of SAMUEL's *house.* MARTHA *stands with her back to the audience. When the four men enter with the body of* SAMUEL *she turns and for a moment stands aghast at the sight of her dead husband. Not until the body is laid full length on the table in front of her does she succumb to her grief. Then she weeps loudly with her head buried in his chest. Three of the men stand back.* DRUMMOND *comes to* MARTHA's *side. Music fades.*

MARTHA: Oh, Samuel, Samuel. Why did you go!

DRUMMOND: I know why Samuel came, Martha. In the end, after all the doubts and questions, he believed that the world we live in tomorrow is what *we* make of it today. He died that those who follow might live their lives more fully.

MARTHA (*stroking the hair from his forehead*): God bless you, dear Samuel. God bless you.

(*The first subdued strains of 'We Shall Overcome' are played. The* SCHOLAR *enters and stands to the other side of* MARTHA *and* DRUMMOND. *He gazes at* SAMUEL *for a moment and then turns to the audience.*)

SCHOLAR: God bless you, indeed, Samuel. Your death was not in vain. You have given to us the faith that WE SHALL OVERCOME.

(*During this brief scene the entire cast has formed up out of sight ready for their last entry. With the Scholar's last words, the cast enters the hall singing 'We Shall Overcome'. They should enter in ranks, with one member of each carrying a banner. The banners will be inscribed with commemorations of great events in the history of the struggle for freedom, both in this country and elsewhere. The banners should arrive in 'historical order', beginning, perhaps with:* 1824, TRADES UNIONS FREED; 1829, METROPLITAN POLICE

FORMED; 1832, GREAT REFORM BILL *and so on right up until the present era;* 1945, INDIA GRANTED INDEPENDENCE, *or* 1967, U.N. CONDEMNS APARTHEID IN SOUTH AFRICA.

The cast are now formed up before the stage for the singing of the final chorus with which The Massacre of Peterloo *ends.)*

WE SHALL OVERCOME

1. We shall overcome,
   We shall overcome,
   We shall overcome some day,
   Oh, deep in my heart I do believe,
   We shall overcome some day.

2. Truth shall make us free,
   Truth shall make us free,
   Truth shall make us free some day
   Oh, deep in my heart I do believe,
   Truth shall make us free some day.

3. We'll walk hand in hand,
   We'll walk hand in hand,
   We'll walk hand in hand some day,
   Oh, deep in my heart I do believe,
   We shall overcome some day.

4. We shall overcome,
   We shall overcome,
   We shall overcome some day,
   Oh, deep in my heart I do believe.
   WE SHALL OVERCOME SOME DAY!

PROJECT PETERLOO

TEACHER'S SECTION

Introduction

Until *The Massacre of Peterloo*, the responsibility I least enjoyed as Head of English was the annual school play. In our drama lessons we had aimed to weave the fabric of a play out of a sensitive exploration of situation and character. We seldom had any prior idea of how the narrative structure would emerge. We hoped that plays would assume a life of their own and dictate their own 'form'. We were therefore set the problem of finding a vital theme out of which we could forge a 'play', suitable for public presentation.

We found our inspiration one ordinary morning when a group of fourth-formers were reading together an account of the Peterloo massacre written by a Manchester reporter in 1819. In it he relates how a vast but peaceable assembly of Lancashire workers and their families, come to St Peter's Field to hear their idol, Henry Hunt, were suddenly and without warning attacked by detachments of Yeomanry and cruelly dispersed. Here, I was convinced, was the theme for our next drama lesson.

That first Peterloo period was unforgettable. The march to the meeting; the cheering and singing; the arrival of Hunt; his brief speech; the assault upon the crowd; the panic and flight of the crowd; the sobbing and groaning of the women; and, over it all, the pathetic tenderness with which the wounded were tended, were all profoundly moving. The lesson bell had rung ten minutes earlier and no one had heard it!

In the days and weeks which followed, the play was created, and at the end of term we presented it to audiences who night after night were visibly moved by its poignancy.

When it was all over as a play it soon became clear that it had very real possibilities as a springboard for extensive project-work.

Its main strengths were and are that it requires the participation of an unusually large number of boys and girls as actors and assistants. (Our original production had involved well over 100 pupils). Indeed, every senior pupil in the school, and a number of juniors, might take part, so that when it came to project-work all pupils would share a common stimulus. Secondly, the play deals with questions which are of concern to a very wide range of subject-teachers, particularly in English, Art, History, Religious Education, and Social Studies. Other departments, such as Music, Woodwork, Needlework, and even perhaps Physical Education would be able to contribute their particular skills at a more practical and immediate level. Hence, in a school intending to present *The Massacre of Peterloo*, and to use it as the basis of project-work, large groups of children and several members of staff might be engaged in the intensive exploration of a single theme which would extend quite naturally over large areas of the secondary curriculum. Finally, the play undoubtedly makes a forceful and intelligible impact upon actors, assistants, and audiences. It is a play to awaken sympathies and excite curiosity and, as such, the study that pupils devote to it will assume a personal and lasting significance.

Mounting the Project

If *The Massacre of Peterloo* is to be the foundation of a project an initial decision will be required as to the kind of project which is to be mounted. Several questions arise. Which pupils are to be involved? All those actually taking part in the play? Or a complete year from which most of the cast is taken? Or, indeed, only one particular class? How extensive shall be the curricula area it is to cover? Shall only English or History be involved, or shall every subject depart-ment which is able to make a contribution be requested to do so? Having decided on the scope of the project, how intensively shall it be·explored? Shall pupils' attention be directed to the immediate social and political context in which the event occurred, or shall this event become the stimulus for a much deeper exploration of what is implied in political action? How much time is to be given to the project both in terms of the proportion of the normal timetable it might claim and of the total period to be given over to it from beginning to completion? The questions of scope, intensity, and timing settled, one final matter arises: shall the normal subject distinctions operate, or shall there be some attempt at integrating the project across the whole curriculum.

This section will offer guidance on these and a number of allied questions.

1. Which Pupils

The play itself requires a cast of not less than eighty pupils. There is virtually no upper limit on the number taking part. The play is ideally suited to the 15 to 17 age-group. Lower sixth- and fifth-formers would probably gain most, but an enthusiastic fourth year would certainly derive a great deal from it. Having chosen the year-groups or forms from which the cast is to be drawn, there is no reason why every pupil in that group should not be involved. The play has principal parts for only forty characters, but the remainder constitute the crowd which in a sense is the most important element in the play. For those who do not in any circumstances enjoy 'acting', there will be a large number of technical and other roles for them to play. There will also be a need for a small group of very young pupils who will act as the children of the workers at St Peter's Field. They will probably not be involved in the kind of project-work recommended here.

The question of which pupils shall undertake the project is comparatively simple, therefore. If it is decided to involve only those who participate in the play, then a whole year-group or a number of different forms could be incorporated in their entirety. There is no reason, however, to limit the work in this way. If the fifth forms, for example, are to present the play, the fourth forms might well do the project. Finally, and depending upon the kind of project-structure adopted, individual pupils can work through the pupils' section at their own pace and at times convenient. Hence the question of who shall take part is entirely a matter of convenience.

2. How Extensive?

How many different subjects can make a real contribution to the project, and what sort of ground will they best cover? The answer to this question will help determine how much time is to be devoted to the project.

History

Peterloo is of such critical historical importance that teachers of History will very likely consider that it has more to offer their subject than any other and that correspondingly they are prepared to devote far more of their subject time to the fullest exploration of its historical significance. In the Pupils' Section, English working-class Radicalism in the period 1789 to 1819 is covered in some detail against the background of the Industrial Revolution and the American and French revolutions. Brief biographical notes are provided on a few leading Radicals such as Thomas Hardy, William Cobbett, Henry Hunt, and Tom Paine. There are a number of questions and suggestions for further work which lead the pupil into personal research and imaginative writing.

Against this general background and Peterloo's place in it, there will be opportunities to explore local Radicalism during the relevant period and to relate it to the social and industrial conditions of the locality.

English

The primary impact upon children's *linguistic* sensibilities will come from Peterloo as drama, but a large number of other skills can be exercised. There are a number of eyewitness accounts to be read and discussed. There are poems to read and to be written, passages to read aloud, and suggestions for the writing of short plays or dialogues. A number of debates or discussions can be held based on some of the controversial questions to which Peterloo and Radicalism give rise. Pupils' attention will occasionally be directed towards particular novels or poems written during this period. Indeed, every aspect of English work can be incorporated.

Religious Education

Some important religious and moral issues arise from *The Massacre of Peterloo*. Towards the end of the pupils' section there are a number of questions relating to the Nonconformist church and the part played by the clergy during the period of Radical unrest. Further questions invite pupils to examine some of the conflicts in personal relationships in the play and to consider the role Christians might play and have played in the face of social injustice.

Art

The Massacre of Peterloo can act as a powerful stimulus to the artistic imagination for it is rich in movement, colour, and detail. If some of the eyewitness accounts are first read to pupils they will more easily visualize and reproduce the scene. There will also be the need to sketch costumes and uniforms, a job which could be undertaken in association with the Needlework department. The exhibition foyer will need to be hung with illustrations, drawings, and paintings and of course the play itself requires a number of fairly elaborate sets. In the section headed 'Personal Folios' a number of pictorial themes have been suggested as a stimulus to art-work.

Social Studies

Any study of Radicalism is bound to raise important social questions and to require the investigation of political and constitutional concepts such as democracy, the franchise, sedition, and public order. Pupils are invited to organize a trial of Henry Hunt which will provide opportunities for the further exploration of what is legitimate public protest and how the attitudes and actions of the authorities help to determine the outcome of popular demonstrations.

Music

Music is incorporated into the play chiefly as 'background' to the massacre, as accompaniment to marching and as part of the finale, when the whole cast sing 'We Shall Overcome'. In so far as the project is concerned, there are a number of recorded industrial folk-ballads to which pupils might listen, and a study could be made of revolutionary and patriotic music as expressed in national anthems, and orchestral music like Malcolm Arnold's 'Peterloo Overture', Shostakovitch's '1905' Symphony, Tchaikovsky's '1812', Beethoven's 'Eroica', and Sibelius's 'Finlandia'. Pupils are invited to compose their own folk-songs based on *The Massacre of Peterloo*.

Apart from the subject work outlined above, the Needlework and Woodwork departments have obvious contributions to make towards the making of costume and properties. Since certain scenes require disciplined drilling and marching, the P.E. department might feel that some time at least could be spent on the preparation of this aspect of the play.

This brief survey of the contributions that various departments might make towards both play and project suggests that during the 'Peterloo' period extensive areas of the curriculum can be mobilized to channel a common interest and achieve a common goal.

In order to judge accurately how many departments might be involved, and to what degree each will devote time to the project, the question of how thoroughly the theme will be explored needs attention. Very briefly the matter resolves itself into a choice between a limited consideration of the immediate context in which the Peterloo massacre occurred, as against a deeper investigation not only of the event itself, and its immediate context, but of the wider questions to which it gives rise. If the former course is adopted, then the History department will retain a special interest in the theme, but other departments might well conclude that their part is not likely to be a very important one.

3. Timing the Project

The Massacre of Peterloo does not require a long preparatory period. It could be completed in half a term. The project will probably prove most relevant if it is timed to coincide with the production period and to overlap the end of the play by a week or two since much of the project's stimulus will derive from the complete experience of having presented the play in performance. The decision as to what proportion of the normal timetable is to be devoted to the project will depend upon the question raised above under the heading *How Extensive?* One possibility to be avoided, of course, is that pupils become too quickly satiated with the project-theme, though if it is properly phased, there should be little danger of this happening.

At this point the administrative implications of Peterloo ought to be discussed. How much 'dislocation' of the normal school routine would be involved in simultaneously putting on the play and mounting a major project? Again, this will depend upon decisions already referred to and upon the structure of the project, the alternative possibilities of which will be discussed in the next section. If the play is presented in 'isolation', then most of the early rehearsing, especially of the small-group scenes, can be done during lunch-hours or for short periods after school. During the third and fourth weeks of the production period pupils in the 'core' of the crowd (i.e. a nucleus of crowd-leaders specially trained to lead later additions of large numbers of pupils) might rehearse in lesson time. In the fifth week the whole crowd will need to rehearse together, probably in school time since the problems of gathering such large groups of children in 'free' time are likely to prove very bewildering. In-school practice of this kind should not require more time than a good double period each day.

The sixth week will present the most difficult problems. At this point the producer has the monumental task of unifying the various components which have until this time been developing independently. Perhaps other staff will be needed to supervise the large groups of children who are awaiting their turn to rehearse, though at this juncture the level of interest and involvement should be sufficient to ensure that the producer has no more than the normal worries associated with putting on a play. If dress rehearsals in the seventh week go according to plan, the out-of-lesson time should not be excessive. During the week of actual performances there should be no reason to disturb normal school routine.

In conclusion, it ought in fairness to be pointed out that before 'Peterloo' is embarked upon, very careful thought should be given to what will be required of the school's administrative machinery. Clearly its presentation requires very careful planning. The producer will find it particularly helpful if he receives at the very outset clear guidance as to how much rearrangement the school is prepared to countenance. Once this understanding is made clear, and the producer and his colleagues embark upon the play, and perhaps the project, they will certainly find that the rewards more than compensate for any short-term inconvenience.

4. Structuring the Project

One final question remains: it concerns structure. Shall the theme be approached from within the conventional subject and timetabling pattern, or shall some attempt be made to achieve an integrated approach? No argument will be advanced here as to which of the two approaches is preferable. There are distinct advantages in both and these should be briefly discussed.

The subject method necessitates the least dislocation: the project theme becomes subject material in the same way that any other topic would. Nor is this approach dependent upon co-operation – individual subject-teachers can proceed with the project irrespective of what their colleagues can manage. Finally, such an approach permits the incorporation of the project material into an existing subject syllabus and as such lends itself to examination. There is no reason, for example, why a study of Peterloo in its historical setting should not constitute a major part of a CSE History Course, particularly if the Mode 3 arrangement is adopted.

On the other hand, many teachers who welcome recent tendencies to integrate studies and unify the curriculum may well regard the Peterloo theme as ideal for this purpose. They might argue that subject-divisions are academic conveniences but hardly a proper basis for the education of the average child who should be helped to apprehend the world of experience as essentially interrelated and unified. The fragmented approach has practical disadvantages too in that children's spans of interest and motivation seldom correlate to our forty-minute periods arbitrarily scattered, subject by subject, across the timetable. The integrated approach, on the other hand, permits children to pursue their own enthusiasms and to learn the intrinsic value of a sustained and intensive exploration of a single topic.

As has already been suggested, this book cannot hope to anticipate every possible approach to project work but some indication, at least, should be given as to how Peterloo might form the substance of an integrated studies project. So far as pupils' work is concerned, the project might aim to have three tangible outcomes:

(1) each pupil to produce a personal folio comprising a thorough exploration of some particular aspect of the theme;

(2) each pupil to prepare some finished written or visual piece of work suitable for display in an exhibition which will accompany the actual presentation of the play to friends and parents;

(3) each pupil to prepare his part in a final mock-trial or debate.

Pupils will begin work on their folios from the time the project is launched. Their display pieces can be prepared nearer the time of performance and the mock-trial or debate can form a follow-up to the project timed to take place within a few days of the play's presentation.

Thus the emphasis will be upon pupil-learning. What would be the role of teachers? Let us envisage a school in which it has been agreed that *all* the time normally devoted to English, History,

R.E., and Social Studies shall be given over to the project. This might amount to nine periods a week. These nine periods might be allocated between three teaching functions:

(1) A background talk, lecture, visit, film-show to *all* pupils undertaking the project, e.g. 'Manchester in 1819'; 'The Industrial Revolution'; 'The Music of Revolution', or the film *Fame is the Spur*. (Two periods).

(2) Workshop or study sessions when the teacher demonstrates or explains particular skills such as note-taking, using source-books, or writing biographical sketches. There would also be the opportunity for examining and discussing relevant material, eyewitness accounts, poems, historical texts. (Three periods).

(3) Finally, the teacher would act in a tutorial capacity, giving individual children help with their folios and display material. Children would thus spend four of the ten periods undertaking personal research in a school or local library under the supervision of teachers who would 'tutor' each child in turn.

What distinguishes the integrated approach is that *all* teachers teach *all* children a single theme. Their function is not then understood so much in terms of the subject they teach as in the mode of learning they encourage, the kind of *self-educative* skills they promote.

PUPILS' SECTION

The Massacre of Peterloo is a documentary play, which means that the events portrayed in it are based on historical fact. Many of you who are taking part in the play or seeing it as members of an audience will already have sensed how tragic an event it was. But it did not take place in a vacuum. Historical events are like people in that if we are to understand them fully we need to know something of the circumstances and conditions in which they were formed. Those of you who have found the Peterloo story moving or interesting may want to understand it more fully or explore more deeply. In the pages which follow you will find suggestions for further work, questions, and material, all related to the Peterloo massacre and the events leading up to it.

Part I: The Age of Revolution

Human society is always in process of change; every generation remarks how things are not as they used to be. But the years 1760–1840 witnessed developments of such fundamental and far-reaching importance that we may accurately call this period the age of revolution.

When George III came to the throne in 1760, England was a stable country. Although the Settlement of 1688 had not given the mass of the people an equal share in government there was nevertheless prosperity, order, and peace in England. English society was a traditional one, too. Its population was small (scarcely double what it had been three centuries before) and despite its considerable trade and colonial expansion, its home industries were largely based in workshops and cottages. Most of its people lived on and worked the land as their forefathers had done for centuries.

In the eighty years which followed, this picture was to change dramatically. The American colonies were to rebel, French society was to undergo a cataclysmic upheaval, and the face of England was to be transformed by the machines, factories, and conurbations created by the Industrial Revolution.

The Industrial Revolution

G. M. Trevelyan described the industrial transformation of England between 1782 and 1832 in these terms:

> The Industrial Revolution is, in its social consequences, mainly destructive. It destroys, in town and country, the forms and pieties of the old English life that could not be harnessed to the new machinery. The Government, while it prohibited all legal and political change as 'Jacobin', urged on the economic revolution. The result was that by 1832 there was scant provision for the political, municipal, educational, or sanitary needs of the population, most of whom were not even tolerably clothed or fed. The laws and institutions had been kept back in one place while the men and women had been moved on to another, where they were living as it were outside society, under a guard of Yeomanry and magistrates.

Mention of Yeomanry and magistrates reminds us at once of Peterloo which was as much about industrial rights for *workers* as about political rights for *citizens*. This was perhaps the most far-reaching effect of the Industrial Revolution: it brought into existence in a comparatively short space of time a new and large class of industrial workers who lived and worked in close proximity. Once this new class became conscious of the fact that prosperity was by no means a benefit shared by all, that for most it resulted in the most intolerable misery and degredation, then the ideas of Tom Paine and the great Radicals who followed him spread like wildfire. Where industrial change was most pronounced, in the great towns of Lancashire, Yorkshire, and the Midlands, there too was to be found the most extensive and enthusiastic support for the gospel of reform.

Monopoly, and the hideous accumulation of capital carry in their own enormity, the seeds of cure. Whatever presses men together, though it may generate some vices, is favourable to the diffusion of knowledge, and ultimately promotive of human liberty. Hence every large workshop and manufactory is a sort of political society, which no act of parliament can silence, and no magistrate disperse.

JOHN THELWALL

(1) What was the population of England and Wales in 1750? Find population figures for each decade until 1850. Draw a chart marked horizontally with the dates and vertically by growth in population. By what percentage did the population increase in the years between 1750 and 1850, and between 1850 and 1950?

(2) The rapid rise in population during this period was a matter of very great concern to social observers. Thomas Malthus was one of the principal voices expressing fear of what would happen if it continued to grow unchecked. Who was Malthus, and to what did he ascribe' the rapid growth in population?

(3) During the years of the Industrial Revolution England became the wealthiest country in the world. On what was this wealth based? What were the principal industries? What did England export? From where did England obtain its supplies?

(4) The Industrial Revolution did not affect all parts of England in the same way. Draw a large map of England and mark those areas in which population grew fastest. Why did these particular areas grow with such speed?

(5) Imagine going to visit a relative in Manchester, Cardiff, Leeds, or Nottingham around 1819. Imagine you have come from the country where your father works as an agricultural labourer. Although the conditions of his life might not be very much better than those of the town-worker, they were certainly very different. Describe your arrival on the outskirts of the town which you overlook from a hill. What sort of landscape do you see?

As you enter the town describe the streets through which you pass. What are the houses like? Are there pavements? drains? street-lights?

Describe your arrival at your relative's house. What is the inside of the house like?

(6) William Cobbett travelled extensively throughout England at this time. When he visited the north of England he was shocked by what he saw:

> Talk of vassals! Talk of villains! Talk of serfs! Are there any of these, or did feudal times ever see any of them, so debased, so absolutely slaves, as the poor creatures who are compelled to work fourteen hours a day, in a heat of eighty-four degrees, and who are liable to punishment for looking out at a window of the factory!

Describe a textile factory in the Manchester area in 1819. What sort of building was it? What were working conditions like! Who were the overseers? What were workers paid and for how long did they work?

(7) The Industrial Revolution was accompanied by extensive and appalling poverty, such as is described in this popular Lancashire ballad which was frequently heard in the years following Waterloo.

> Aw'm a poor cotton wayver as many a one knows,
> Aw've nowt t'eat in the house, an' aw've wore out me clo'es,
> Me clogs are both brokken an stockins aw've none,
> Yo'd hardly gie tuppence for all aw've got on.
>   Yo'd think it were hard to be sent in the world
>   To clem★ an' do best 'at yo can.
>
> Our parish church parson kept tellin us long
> We'd see better times if we'f but howd our tongue.
> Aw've howden me tongue till aw've near lost me breath,
> An' aw think in me heart he means to starve us to death.
>   Aw know he lives weel wi' backbitin the Devil,
>   But he never picked o'er in his life.

★ Clem = Starve

We held on six weeks thinking each day were t'last
We tarried an' shifted till now we're quite fast.
We lived on nettles while nettles was good,
An' Wayterloo porritch were t'best of us food.
    Av'm tellin ye true, aw can find folk enoo
    That are livin no better nor me.

For those who could not find work or who found their wages too
low, there was the Poor Law or 'outdoor relief' as it was called.
Under this system the Parish made small payments which were
usually pegged to the price of bread. But even with such 'relief'
many were unable to cope and for them there was the dreadful fate
of the workhouse. These places were deliberately designed to be so
distasteful that the poor would agree to enter them only after life
outside had become utterly intolerable. George Crabbe, a notable
poet of this time, wrote:

You have placed your poor, your pitiable few;
There, in one house, throughout their lives to be,
The pauper-palace which they hate to see;
That great building, that high-bounding wall,
Those bare-worn walks, that lofty thund'ring hall!
That large loud clock, which tolls each dreaded hour,
Those gates and locks, and all those signs of power;
It is a prison, with a milder name,
Which few inhabit without dread or shame.

Write a short story or a poem which expresses the feelings of an
old widow who, driven by poverty, is forced to give up her home
and enter the workhouse.

(8) In 1819 the average length of life was much shorter than it is
today. What sort of illnesses and diseases were common at this time?
What sort of medical help was available to the sick? What sort of
hospitals existed? Why did so many babies die at birth? What sort

of official help was provided to the sick during their periods of illness?

(9) Elementary Education in England was not generally available until 1870. Nevertheless, a large proportion of ordinary people did receive some form of basic education, as witnessed by the large public which read books like *The Rights of Man*, *Gulliver's Travels* or *Pilgrim's Progress*. Education for the working classes at this time was of three kinds broadly: self-education at home or in societies and clubs; charity-schooling; or Sunday-schooling.

Imagine yourself a pupil at a church school in 1820. In what ways would such a school be different from the school which you attend at present?

(10) But most children in the industrial parts of England had little schooling and spent most of their waking lives in factories, even though parents were often loth to let their children work in such places. A Manchester father whose son had been killed in a factory accident declared:

> I have had seven boys, but if I had seventy-seven I should never send one to a cotton factory. . . . One great objection that I have is, that their morals are very much corrupted. . . . They have to be in the factories from six in the morning till eight at night, consequently they have no means of instruction . . . there is no good example shown them. . . .

Find out all that you can about child labour in the early nineteenth century. How long each day did children work, and what sort of work did they do? What was the apprenticeship system?

(Read those parts of George Crabbe's poem 'The Borough' which tell of the cruel Peter Grimes.)

Women in the Industrial Revolution

'Before the Industrial Revolution women spun and wove in their houses, brewed the ale, looked after the pigs and fowls. Specialization extinguished this life and the women who helped to spin and weave the nation's clothes under the new system, left their homes for the factory.'

Although the Hammonds' description of how the Industrial Revolution affected women is largely accurate, it would be wrong to imagine that it brought no benefits. In the domestic industries women were bound to their husbands' employment and although they might play an important part in production, their labour was not separately rewarded. In the factories they received their own wages and their earning power did much to improve their social standing.

(Women's wages were generally much lower than men's, so that a 25 year-old woman cotton worker earned 8s. 5d. per week in 1833, while a man of the same age earned 17s. 3d. per week).

Nor were all the factories the hell-holes that have so frequently been described. Some were well-ventilated, wholesome places, and women often preferred the work of the factory to the drudgery of the home. But none of this should blind us to many of the cruel abuses that were practised. Perhaps the most appalling work under-taken by women was that of coal mining, which often taxed their strength beyond endurance. Robert Bald described the women he saw in the Whitehaven mines in 1813:

All of the same description, ragged and beastly in their appear-ance and with a shameless indecency in their behaviour, which, awestruck as one was by the gloom and loneliness around me, had something quite frightful in it, and gave the place the character of hell. All the women we met with were distinguished by an extra-ordinary wickedness; immoderate labour and a noxious atmos-phere had marked their countenances with the signs of disease and decay; they were mostly half-naked, blackened all over with dirt, and altogether so miserably disfigured and abused, that they looked like a race fallen from the common rank of men and doomed as in a kind of purgatory, to wear away their lives in these dismal shades.

In the years immediately preceding Peterloo, women workers, in the north particularly, began to organize themselves into trade unions and women's clubs though their chief purpose was to lend moral support to their menfolk in their struggle for greater justice. When William Cobbett went to Blackburn in the year of Peterloo, he was greeted by the local Female Union, whose most bitter complaint was on behalf of their children:

'We are daily cut to the heart to see them greedily devour the coarse food that some would scarcely give to their swine.'

There was little that Cobbett could offer by way of help, and it ought to be remembered that the first fatal injury on St Peter's Field was that of a woman.

(11) Write a conversation between a factory master who is recruiting women workers and a country woman who helps her husband, a weaver in their own cottage. Make the factory master as persuasive as you can, and suggest why the woman might hesitate to accept his offer of factory work.

(12) See if you can find what a Manchester working-class family might be earning in 1819. Remember that children worked too. Then make a list of a family's principal expenses each week: rent, food, fuel, etc. (Ivy Pinchbeck's *Women Workers and the Industrial Revolution*, or the Hammonds' *The Skilled Labourer 1760–1832* will be of great help if you can obtain copies from your local library).

Britain and Foreign Revolution

Between 1756 and 1763 England and France fought a bitter war over who should rule the vast and bountiful North American continent. Paradoxically, England's victory lead to a major defeat twenty years later, for when the colonists no longer required the protection of the mother country against the French their hopes turned to their own independence. Had English policy towards the colonists been wiser, war might have been avoided, but when in 1767 England

imposed the notorious tea taxes the Americans retorted, 'No taxation without representation', and were prepared to fight for the
principle.

What happened in Boston was bound to have repercussions at
home. The British Government regarded the American colonists as
subjects of the crown, with no more right to a say in government
than the mass of British subjects had. If the American claim to
representation were to succeed the flood-gates of reform would open
wide. Thus the Government took repressive penal measures against
the rebels, who retaliated, and in 1774 the Battle of Lexington
sparked off the War of Independence.

In the struggle which followed, American forces under George
Washington's brilliant leadership overcame the armies of the Crown
and by 1783 American Independence was finally established. This
costly and ill-conducted war was a major setback for the King and
his Government. What is more, the people of England had been
given an example of a successful struggle for democratic rights. This
example of America was bound to influence Radicals in Britain. It
was to prove an even stronger influence in France for many French-
men had fought alongside the American rebels and later took back
the ideas of democratic rights to their home country. In France the
Government was even more repressive and unrepresentative than in
England but within a few years of American independence the
French monarchy was toppled in a more dramatic and violent up-
surge of popular Radicalism.

The French Revolution

That which I glory in, in the French Revolution, is this: that it
has upheld and propagated as a principle of that Revolution, that
ancient abuses are not by their antiquity converted into virtues
. . . that man has rights which no statutes or usages can take away
. . . that thought ought to be free . . . that intellectual beings are
entitled to the use of their intellects . . . that one order of society
has no right, how many years soever they have been guilty of the

pillage, to plunder and oppress the other parts of the community.... These are the principles that I admire, and that cause me notwithstanding all its excesses, to exult in the French Revolution.

JOHN THELWALL

The story of the French Revolution – its causes and the course it followed – is a fascinating one, but our interest in it must be confined to the effects it had upon the growing radical movement in England. In 1789 the angry Parisian mob stormed the Bastille, the grim fortress which symbolized the tyranny of the old order. That attack and the events which followed immediately upon it were greeted, at least at first, by many English people of all classes as a major step towards the kind of limited liberty that had already been achieved in England. Charles James Fox, the moderate Whig, hailed the events of 1789 with the words: 'How much the greatest thing it is that has ever happened and how much the best!' But with the passing of time it became clear that the early idealism of 'Liberty, Equality, and Fraternity' was to degenerate into a cruel and uncontrolled bloodbath.

As early as 1790 Edmund Burke published his *Reflections on the French Revolution* which roused traditional conservatives to an even greater loathing of reformers. In 1791 the Birmingham house of Joseph Priestley, the Nonconformist advocate of Parliamentary reform, was burned to the ground by a 'Church and King' mob encouraged in their criminality by those forces of the establishment who should have been the strongest upholders of law and order – the Justices of the Peace and the local clergy. Other Dissenters were similarly victimized but their continued exclusion from the franchise was to become part of a bigger cause – the radical working-class movement.

The first great prophet of this movement was undoubtedly the Norfolk-born shoemaker, Tom Paine. Paine was a Quaker who had journeyed to America in 1774 and thrown his support behind the cause of the American rebels. George Washington was one of those principally affected by Paine's ideas. For years he had nightly toasted the British King and Constitution, but after reading Paine's early pamphlet, *Common Sense*, he had to admit the force of Paine's logic and gave up the practice! Paine was an ardent republican, a staunch egalitarian, and a pamphleteer with a compelling and passionate style. He had later joined the revolutionary forces in France, whose revolution he had praised in his famous book, *The Rights of Man*, written as a reply to Edmund Burke. Paine's masterpiece, with its attacks upon social inequality, corrupt government, the hereditary principle, monarchy, and poverty, argued that all rights emanated from the people and that those who held power on the basis of privilege or property were usurpers who should be overthrown, if necessary by force. It further advocated that the people's welfare was the responsibility of the State, which should provide free education, a health service, marriage and family allowances, and a host of other social benefits. Not surprisingly, it was banned as a seditious publication, and those who were found printing, selling, or distributing it were imprisoned or transported. Paine's book nevertheless became the political bible of the working classes. Cheap editions flourished, and although Paine failed to achieve the republican revolution he had called for, his ideas were to inspire radical discussion for half a century and more. Through Tom Paine the spirit of the French Revolution seeped into England. He died in America in 1809, but his bones were returned to England by William Cobbett in 1819, the year of the Peterloo Massacre.

(1) What was the Boston Tea-Party? What were the principles underlying the conflict which broke out in Boston?

(2) The American Declaration of Independence speaks of 'certain truths which we hold to be self-evident'. Find a copy of this document and list the self-evident truths it speaks of.

(3) Draw up a chronological table of the chief events which occurred in France between the storming of the Bastille in 1789 and the declaration of war against England in 1793.

(4) If you live in Birmingham try to discover from local records what actually happened during the terrible riots of 1791.

(5) 'O, Paine! next to God, how infinitely are millions beholden to you for the small remnant of their liberties . . . it was reserved to you to wave the celestial banners of the rights of man over the tottering bastiles of Europe and to break the shackles of despotism from the ankles of millions!'

Such was the view of one of Paine's admirers (not an Englishman). Write a short biographical sketch of Tom Paine.

(7) What do each of the following terms mean? Make up sentences which illustrate their use.

(a) radicalism	(g) a moderate
(b) democracy	(h) franchise
(c) conservatism	(i) republican
(d) representation	(j) egalitarian
(e) statute	(k) usurper
(f) political prisoner	(l) seditious

Three Famous Ninetenth-Century Radicals

The roll-call of English Radicals is a long and impressive one. Tom Paine, William Cobbett, Major Cartwright, John Thelwall, Thomas Hardy, John Knight, Samuel Bamford, Henry Hunt were all prominent popular leaders during the years before the Peterloo massacre. We have already considered the unique part played by Tom Paine, perhaps the greatest of them all. We shall now pay some attention to three others, all of whom affected the atmosphere in which the Manchester meeting took place in 1819.

Thomas Hardy

In March 1792, a small group of London working men met at The Bell in Exeter Street off the Strand in London to discuss the important subject of Parliamentary Reform. A few weeks later they set up the London Corresponding Society, the most important principle of which was 'That the number of our members be unlimited'. Its secretary was Thomas Hardy, like Tom Paine, a shoemaker, and an ardent Dissenter.

The London Corresponding Society grew rapidly, so that before the year was out it claimed well over 2,000 members. Its programme was Universal Suffrage and Annual Parliaments, both of which were to be demanded at Peterloo and later by the Chartists. But it was also an educational society. In the exchange between members of letters containing opinions on a wide range of burning topical issues, in the publication of pamphlets, the organization of debates and the collection of subscriptions, it was to form the organizational basis of much of later working-class Radicalism. But the Government, as we have seen, was alarmed by the spread of Jacobin theories and on May 12th 1794 Thomas Hardy was arrested on a charge of high treason. His home was ransacked, and his poor wife, who was pregnant, was so disturbed by the commotion that she later died in child-birth.

Hardy and his friends were then committed to the Tower to await their fate. (Traitors were still liable to a sentence whereby they were hanged, cut down while still alive, disembowelled and their entrails burned before their faces.) The Government's case broke down, however, and Hardy was acquitted. The London crowd who had followed the trial with mounting concern and anger were jubilant. Hardy rode in triumph through the streets.

Hardy now largely withdrew from active political life and returned to his business, which had almost collapsed, but when he set up again in a shop in Clerkenwell, customers thronged for his services. He retired in 1815 and for the remainder of his life was supported by a small group of wealthy Radicals. He died in 1832 at the age of 81.

William Cobbett

The years following the victory of Waterloo were troubled ones. At times it must have seemed as if the very social system was in danger of collapse, and yet national insurrection was averted. One of the most influential of Radical spokesmen during this period was undoubtedly William Cobbett, whose moderation, humanity, and intelligence were put to the service of reform rather than revolution. 'Old Corruption' as Cobbett called the unreformed Parliament, had to be swept away and all means to this end were legitimate – *save those of violence.*

In his early life, Cobbett, who came from a comfortable farming family, had shared the views of the Tory land-owning class, but the French wars were to bring distress and hunger on such a scale that Cobbett's humanity was enlisted for all times on the side of the poor and unrepresented. In serving the interests of the common people, he was an outspoken opponent of all abuses, especially borough-mongering, sinecures, and enclosures. He abhorred industrialism and the grasping materialism it gave birth to. Although a romantic in that he longed to see England return to an almost mythical golden age of social harmony, he nevertheless brought to the attention of the powerful middle classes the extent of the suffering and poverty to which the people were subject. He more than any other public figure interested the middle classes in the cause of reform, and once their support was gained, the great Reform Acts of 1832, 1867, and 1884 passed in what seems in retrospect like an inevitable succession.

Cobbett's literary gifts were outstanding, and in his *Rural Rides* he draws a detailed and evocative picture of English life a few years before Peterloo. His most influential publication, however, was undoubtedly *The Political Register*, a periodical which ruthlessly and satirically exposed the hypocrisies of his age. But his 'Register' was expensive and when in 1816 he dramatically reduced the price from over 1s. to 2d. his readership increased considerably; and his popularity among the working classes was for ever secure.

In 1817 under the threat of the Six Acts, Cobbett went for safety to America, but he returned two years later and was active in the reform movement until his death in 1835.

Henry Hunt

> With Henry Hunt we'll go, we'll go,
> With Henry Hunt we'll go;
> We'll raise the cap of liberty,
> In spite of Nadin Joe.

One of the minor misfortunes of Peterloo was that Henry Hunt was prevented from delivering his speech. It might well have been a masterpiece, for Hunt was above all an orator – never more effective than when confronted by a vast open-air assembly gathered to hear their bitterest grievances and fondest aspirations articulated. Hunt seldom disappointed. He was to the spoken word what Cobbett was to the written: an engaging, lucid and passionate exponent.

But his service to the Radical movement was not without blemish. Many of those who knew him best speak of his vanity, contemptuousness, ruthlessness and egotism. Hunt was not interested in organizations and committees; he was primarily concerned to build up a vast personal following so that wherever he chose to appear he could count on an enormous and adoring audience. Such was his reception in Manchester on August 16th 1819 but in the scuffles which followed the arrest of Hunt and his party, he bore himself with dignity and even courage. When later in 1819 he returned to London he was greeted by a crowd of some 300,000 cheering citizens.

Hunt, like Cobbett, was a gentleman farmer. In 1812 he contested a Bristol constituency and fired the local electorate with his passionate addresses. But they did not elect him. In the agitation which followed the end of the war with France, Hunt was continually upon the hustings. In November 1816, he addressed a vast gathering in London's Spa Fields. In discussing the extensive unemployment in the capital and elsewhere, he asked: what was the cause of the want of employment, and answered: Taxation. What was the cause of taxation? Corruption. Everything that concerned their subsistence or comforts was taxed. Was not their loaf taxed? Was not their beer taxed? Was not everything they ate, drank, wore and even said taxed? They (taxes) were imposed by a borough-mongering faction who thought of nothing but oppressing the people, and subsisting on the plunder wrung from their miseries.

When in 1817 Cobbett left for America, Hunt remained at home, despite the threats of the Six Acts and the suspension of Habeas Corpus. His following grew and when it was announced that he would be the principal speaker at St Peter's Field, the attendance of large and enthusiastic crowds was assured. The part played by 'Orator' Hunt at that meeting is well known and related in the play, *The Massacre of Peterloo*. After the Manchester meeting, Hunt was arrested, charged, and imprisoned but he continued to fight for the Radical cause and was even to denounce the 1832 Reform Act as a betrayal of the working classes. Hunt was often dubbed 'The Champion of Liberty', and although his motives might not always have been idealistic and unself-seeking, he nevertheless voiced the grievances of the masses and often gave them the heart to continue their struggle.

The Era of Unrest, 1789-1819

It is sometimes suggested that the rise of democracy in England has been a peaceable process. Nothing could be farther from the truth. In the thirty years before Peterloo, from the date of the storming of the Bastille, England was in a state of almost continual social turmoil. Indeed the Nottingham Food riots which occurred in the year before the French Revolution (butchers' shops were raided and their ledgers burned in the market-place) were by no means an unusual occurrence and in the years which followed similar riots took place in Newcastle, Wisbech, Cornwall, Cambridge, Witney, Binford, and Wells. Any sharp rise in the price of basic foodstuffs was accompanied by such outbreaks. In a score of different towns supplies were seized on their way to market and sold at a 'just price'. In 1795

London's Albion Flour Mills were burned to the ground as a protest against the high price of bread.

At the same time as the food riots the country was flooded with cheap editions of Tom Paine's *The Rights of Man*, and the Corresponding Societies were steadily growing in popularity. The authorities grew increasingly alarmed and retaliated with sternly repressive measures. In 1792 a Royal Proclamation was issued against seditious publications and anti-Paine riots were 'sponsored' throughout the country. In December 1792:

> The effigy of Thomas Paine was, with great solemnity, drawn on a sledge from Lincoln Castle to the gallows, and then hanged amidst a vast multitude of spectators. In the evening a large fire was made under the effigy, which was consumed to ashes, amidst the acclamations of many hundreds of people.

As a further 'attack' upon the spread of Jacobin ideas, the Press was daily filled with grisly accounts of what was happening just across the channel in France. In 1795 after an incident in which the King himself was booed by a hostile London crowd and his carriage window smashed by a stone, the Government passed two Acts making it a treasonable offence to incite contempt of the King or Constitution and forbidding meetings of more than fifty persons without the consent of a magistrate. Habeas Corpus was suspended and scores of Radical leaders arrested and held without trial.

In 1797 there were serious mutinies among the Fleet at Spithead and Nore, and in the following year an Irish priest, Father O'Coigly, was executed, having been apprehended on his way to France with letters for delivery to the French revolutionary leaders. By 1799 nearly all the Radical leaders had either fled the country or were in gaol. In a final determined attempt to quell all signs of rebellion the Pitt Government passed its infamous Combination Laws which forbade trade-union activity. So worried indeed were they that they undertook a massive programme of barrack-building throughout the country, so that by 1816 troops were stationed in every town in the country, and 'the English people held down by force'.

The opening year of the nineteenth century witnessed further widespread distress and unrest. Napoleon's boycott of the British Isles greatly reduced trade and the price of food reached unprecedented levels. Despite the Poor Law which allocated relief according to the price of bread, poverty was widespread. Further food riots occurred throughout the country, and in April 1801 the Government again suspended Habeas Corpus and renewed the Seditious Meetings Act.

Despite these measures, midnight meetings, drilling, oath-taking ceremonies and 'seditious' publications were common, especially in the large northern towns of Sheffield, Leeds, and Huddersfield, as well as in London.

One of the foremost leaders of popular rebellion at this time was Colonel Marcus Despard, who attempted to form a revolutionary army, and who as a result was hanged in 1803. As he stood upon the scaffold he uttered these words:

> I wish you my fellow-citizens, health, happiness, and prosperity; although I shall not live to experience the blessings of the godlike change, be assured, citizens, that the period will come, and that speedily, when the glorious cause of liberty shall effectually triumph . . .

The Luddites

> Could we obtain our food by work,
> Would labour like the hardy turk;
> But all our hopes from thence are fled,
> And we now pine for want of bread.
>
> Our children tho' to us most dear,
> Must die for want, we greatly fear;
> Unless some human generous heart,
> Some food for them to us impart.

Could you our habitations see,
The seats of abject misery;
We think you would afford us aid,
Till we return unto our trade.

On heaven and you we now depend,
And trust in you we've found a friend,
And what you give, God will re-pay,
Both here and in the Judgement day.

(Luddite broadsheet, 1812)

We have already seen how the advent of the power-machine and the factory were to change the character of our country. They were not introduced, however, without bitter and often violent opposition. The years 1811–15 were war years and bad years indeed for the working classes. As we have already seen, Trades Unions were forbidden and Parliament refused to grant workers a minimum wage. In such conditions it is not surprising that men unable to achieve their legitimate ends by peaceful means should resort to violence. Chief among those who sought to redress their wrongs by direct action were the Luddites.

Luddites set about the destruction of machinery which they considered the cause of their depressed condition. They were generally skilled men working in small textile workshops and finding it increasingly difficult to compete with the factories operating with cheap female and child labour. In the dead of night, small bands of men in Lancashire, Yorkshire, or Nottinghamshire, would steal out to the factories and destroy the power-looms and shearing-frames.

They were desperate men but also courageous, for death was the certain consequence of arrest. Many died at the hands of the troops. They were not, however, indiscriminate wreckers. Well-disciplined on the whole, their targets were factories belonging to employers who paid low wages, and they seldom struck without first issuing the factory-master with a solemn warning:

> We Hear in Formed that you got Shear in mee sheens (i.e. Shearing Machines) and if you Dont Pull them Down in a Forght Nights time Wee will pull them Down for you Wee will you Damd infernold Dog. And Bee four Almighty God we will pull down all the Mills that leave Heany Shearing me Shens in. We will cut out Hall your Damd Hearts as Do Keep them and We will meock the rest Heat them or else We will Searve them the Seam.

Hence by the year 1812 the country stood on the verge of popular revolution. Luddist insurrection was at its peak, food riots were extensive and as the culmination of these mounting disorders, the Prime Minister, Perceval, was assassinated in the lobby of the House of Commons. Although the murder was not politically inspired (Perceval's slayer was insane), the news of his death was received with unashamed joy. In one northern town a witness describes how a man 'came running down the street, leaping into the air, waving his hat round his head, and shouting with frantic joy: "Perceval is shot, hurrah! Perceval is shot, hurrah!"' John Bellingham, the assassin, was cheered as he went to the gallows and the Government, fearful of further demonstrations, decided not to afford Perceval a public funeral.

In the same year, Major Cartwright, the veteran Radical leader, founded the Hampden Clubs which were to spread radical ideas throughout the country. Cartwright himself undertook extensive speaking tours especially in those regions where Luddism was most in evidence. When in 1815 peace was finally achieved with France, a further period of violent unrest began at home.

(1) Food riots were common in England for forty years between 1790 and 1830. Can you find any evidence of such riots having occurred in your locality during this period? What form did they take? Who led them? What action did the authorities take to suppress them?

(2) Imagine yourself a reporter on a London newspaper in 1795.

Describe the 'attack' upon the King's carriage as he rode towards Parliament. (Contemporary newspapers will give a detailed account of this incident.)

(3) What is Habeas Corpus? Why is it essential to liberty? Why would the Government have sought to suspend it?

(4) The authorities were not totally insensitive to the hardship caused by rising food prices. In 1795 a group of ratepayers in the village of Speenhamland devised a system of aid for the poor. How did it work? What were its effects?

(5) Find out all you can about Colonel Marcus Despard. What sort of man was he? Would you have placed any trust in him?

(6) Describe a night attack upon a mill as if you were one of the party. Remember that many mills at this time were surrounded by high walls and that once the alarm was given troops would soon arrive. (There is an account of such a raid in Charlotte Brontë's novel *Shirley*.)

(7) If you live in Lancashire, Yorkshire or the Midlands, go to your town or county library and ask to see any local histories which might contain accounts of Luddite activity in your area. Summarize them briefly.

(8) Why were the Hampden Clubs so called? How did they differ from the Corresponding Societies?

The Years before Peterloo, 1815-19

E. P. Thompson, whose book, *The Making of the English Working Class*, is a scholarly and exciting study, describes the four years following Waterloo as 'the heroic years of popular Radicalism'. He describes its chief characteristics as 'intransigent opposition to the Government, contempt for the weakness of the Whigs; opposition to restrictions upon political liberties; open exposure of corruption and the Pitt system; and general support for Parliamentary reform'. We might add to this list outright opposition to the Corn Laws which served to artificially maintain a high level of bread prices.

In the months which followed Waterloo, thousands of troops, tired and ill-kempt, arrived home to swell the 'army' of the unemployed and the distressed. Wellington had been rewarded by his country with a gift of £400,000 with which to purchase a mansion and estate. His men were neglected by comparison. One of those who had fought the French, a sailor, Cashman, had been wounded nine times but the back pay he was owed was denied him and money which he had entrusted to the naval authorities for payment to his mother had never reached her. Naturally he was bitterly resentful and during one of the Spa Fields Riots in 1816 he attacked a gunsmith's shop. For this 'crime' he was executed but so inflamed were the people that the scaffold had to be fenced off and surrounded by a huge force of constables. His death was a defiant one, and for several hours after his execution there was an ominous atmosphere in the streets of London.

The Spa Fields Meeting, was not by any means entirely violent. Indeed the main body of the meeting, addressed by Henry Hunt, was a sort of rehearsal for the St Peter's Field rally three years later. Vast crowds gathered; the speakers were confident and popular, the causes were the same. The chief difference between the two meetings lay in their mode of dispersal: the Spa Fields audience returned to their homes safe and heartened.

The year 1817 was filled with rumours of sedition and insurrection. The Prince Regent's carriage was attacked – as his father's had been twenty years before. Government spies and informers frightened the authorities with reports of armed detachments preparing themselves with military type precision. The most famous of these Government spies was W. J. Richards, or Oliver as he was simply known. He gained the confidence of most of the leading Radicals and was admitted to their secret discussions. Indeed, he was frequently elected into positions of responsibility and was often to be heard pleading the Radical case from platforms and hustings.

Among those he contracted to discuss plans for the overthrow of the Government was one, Jeremy Brandreth, who was to take charge of the rising planned to take place in the small Derbyshire town of Pentridge. But Oliver had given the local magistrates good warning, and in the days which followed they waited in readiness.

On the night of June 9th 1817 two or three hundred Derbyshire villagers armed with scythes, pikes, bludgeons and a few guns, set out to march to Nottingham demanding arms and support as they went. At one farm, Brandreth demanded entry and the surrender of arms, but he was refused access, and in retaliation, shot and killed a servant. This was the only bloodshed that night.

Spurred on by Oliver's assurances that London awaited the sign and would flare into rebellion, Brandreth and his dwindling band of followers planned to march to the capital, having first 'captured' Nottingham.

They arrived the following morning in Nottingham, but the populace ignored them. Brandreth, embittered and angered, was arrested and his fleeing followers rounded up by the troops. Brandreth was executed and thus ended the Pentridge Rising. The Radicals had learned a vital lesson, however: to avoid violence and to seek their ends by peaceable means. Such was the mood of those who convened the meeting at St Peter's Field on August 16th 1819.

(1) What were the Corn Laws? Why were they introduced? What were their effects?

(2) Write an account of Cashman's life as a sailor in the naval wars against France. Describe his behaviour and feelings on the day of the attack upon the gunsmith's shop and as he faced execution.

(3) Imagine yourself one of Brandreth's followers on the night of June 9th 1817. Describe your departure from Pentridge, the killing of the farm servant, your arrival in Nottingham, and the final arrest of you and your companions.

Manchester before Peterloo

Robert Southey wrote of Manchester in 1807: 'A place more destitute of all interesting objects is not easy to conceive.' The huge population of this vast growing town were: 'crowded together in narrow streets, the houses all built of brick and blackened with smoke; frequent buildings among them as large as convents, without their antiquity, without their beauty, without their holiness; where you hear from within . . . the everlasting din of machinery; and where when the bell rings it is to call wretches to their work instead of their prayers.'

Manchester was a town without proper local administration or representation in Parliament. Its overriding purpose seemed to be that of amassing wealth as quickly as possible without any concern for the consequences. And yet its population grew at an alarming rate. In 1801 it had 102,000 inhabitants. By 1821 this figure had increased by over 80 per cent to 187,000. As the Hammonds have observed: 'It looks as if the Peels and the Ark-wrights had only to stamp on the ground to turn empty valleys into swarming lines of workpeople.' The 'Peels and the Arkwrights' were the employers whose power and influence steadily increased as the Industrial Revolution proceeded. Their large and crowded factories gradually replaced the old-style work-shops and as a result those who worked in them 'formed a compact body with common aims among whom combination was easy'.

Manchester was the unrivalled centre of the cotton industry for which Lancashire was ideally suited. It was a county of flowing streams to drive Arkwright's machines, of cheap coal for the later steam-engines, of damp air in which cotton processing was easiest, and with access to Liverpool, the great Atlantic port. Some idea of the growth of the cotton industry can be gained from the figures for the import to Great Britain of cotton-wool, the raw material used on which the factories depended. In 1764, only 4,000 lb. were imported. By 1833 this amount had risen to 303,000 lb. Accompanying this increasing consumption of raw cotton was a developing technology, new inventions which raised output and reduced the need for labour. Kay, Hargreaves, Arkwright, Cartwright, and Crompton were some of the great inventors of the age. Their machines were to affect most depressingly the hand-loom weavers who had worked for generations in home and workshop and who now struggled to maintain a decent standard of living. In 1799 the weavers of Manchester petitioned Parliament with complaints of falling wages. The cloth which had earned them 6½d. a yard in 1792 now only fetched 2d. A later Committee of the House of Commons shewed the position graphically in the following table of weavers' wages and what they would purchase of flour, oatmeal, potatoes, and meat between 1797 and 1832.

YEARS	AVERAGE WAGE	WHAT WAGE BUYS
1797–1804	26s. 8d.	281 lb.
1804–1811	20s.	238 lb.
1811–1818	14s. 7d.	131 lb.
1818–1825	8s. 9d.	108 lb.
1825–1832	6s. 4d.	83 lb.

Understandably the weavers were anxious to persuade Parliament to stabilize wages, but Parliament refused to intervene. The weavers, having unsuccessfully petitioned Parliament, organized a widespread strike and demanded an immediate increase in wages of 33⅓ per cent. But the authorities did not give way. They were convinced that wages should find their own natural level in a free market. To interfere with such matters was an infringement of individual liberty. The weavers, who had always avoided political action, now saw that the only way to improve their position was through a reformed Parliament, brought about, if needs be, by widespread protest and demonstrations. When in 1808 a further appeal for a Minimum Wage was rejected by Parliament, riots followed and one man was shot dead by the troops. 'Machine-lifting' became commonplace and in 1808 Rochdale prison was burned down. Between 1811 and 1813 Lancashire Luddism was particularly virulent. Houses and factories were destroyed in Ashton-under-Lyne, Eccles, Middleton, and Stockport, where rioters fired upon troops and were in turn shot at and killed. In Manchester there were serious disturbances, and the authorities became increasingly apprehensive as to the possibility of an organized uprising. More than one observer at the time felt that if England was to be convulsed in revolution it would begin in Manchester.

The magistrates charged with the maintenance of public order were only half capable of stemming the unrest. It is true that men, women, and children were hanged, transported, and imprisoned, but the riots continued and in 1818 a massive strike of cotton spinners took place in Manchester. A factory owner, a Mr Gray, recommended strong action against the strikers: 'Nothing is more unwise in my opinion than to allow the lower orders to feel their strength, and to extend their communications with each other without restraint. Allow them to go on uninterrupted and they daily become more licentious.'

Later that year the strike was broken, chiefly through the intervention of General Byng, whose firmness and courtesy so impressed the strikers. He it was who had reduced the great Blanketeers March from Manchester to London into something of a farce the year before. The magistrates were not altogether sure that his methods would always work, however, and there were some among them who were of the opinion that the time was approaching for a show of decisive force. They were to have their way two years later at St Peter's Field.

The year 1819 was one of particular distress in Lancashire. The Radical leaders resolved to step up their activities, to bring to bear upon an indifferent House of Commons, the most irresistable evidence of popular feeling and the power of the Radicals to mobilize that feeling into constructive and peaceable political channels. They were determined to prove their worthiness for a share in the Government of the country.

Henry Hunt, who was undoubtedly the most popular of the great national radicals, was invited to speak at a projected open-air meeting

to be held on St Peter's Field. He agreed to attend, and even went
so far as to offer himself for arrest before the meeting took place.
But the magistrates had no grounds on which to take him. Hunt
and his followers were thus convinced that their meeting would be
legal and that those who attended would be unmolested. Excitement and tension rose as the day of the meeting approached. Notices
and announcements appeared throughout Manchester and the surrounding districts. Contingents from a hundred towns and villages
were expected. If all went well it might prove to be one of the most
impressive political demonstrations for years. Imagine the satisfaction the organizers must have felt when they awoke on the morning
of August 16th to see the sun rising into a blue and cloudless sky.

(1) For what were Kay, Hargreaves, Arkwright, Cartwright, and
Crompton famous? Briefly describe each of their inventions and give
some indication of how they affected the growth of the cotton
industry.

(2) What was the Blanketeers March of 1817? Why was it such
a dismal failure?

(3) Imagine yourself a Manchester radical leader in 1819. Write a
respectful letter to Henry Hunt inviting him to speak at your projected meeting on St Peter's Field. Write a letter of reply as if from
Henry Hunt.

(4) Describe Manchester in the early morning of August 16th
1819. Write as one who has lived there all his life and who, despite
its ugliness and squalor, still regards it with affection.

Part II: Writers Describe Peterloo

The Manchester Man

There are only one or two passages in fictional literature which
narrate the happenings of August 16th 1819. The extract which
follows is taken from *The Manchester Man* by Mrs G. Linnaeus Banks,
published in 1876. It describes the atmosphere before the charge of

the Yeomanry. Mrs Banks also suggests that the massacre was due largely to the prejudices of one important official, and that the Yeomen might have acted with less brutality had they not drunk so much in the few hours before the meeting.

About nine o'clock the people began to assemble from all quarters on the open ground near St Peter's Church – not blood-thirsty roughs, but men, women and children, drawn thither for a sight of a holiday spectacle. True, of the collective eighty thous-and, though there were many thousands of earnest, thinking men who went to grapple with important questions, yet no such mighty gathering could be without its leaven of savagery and mischief.

But those who went from the mills and the workshops, the hills and the valleys around Manchester, walking in procession, with bugles playing and gay banners flying, though they might look haggard, pinched and care-worn, made no attempt to look de-plorable, or excite compassion. They wore their Sunday suits and clean neckties; and by the side of fustian and corduroy walked the coloured prints and stuffs of wives and sweethearts, who went as for a gala-day, to break the dull monotony of their lives, and to serve as a guarantee of peaceable intention.

Such at least was the main body, marshalled in Middleton by stalwart, stout-hearted Samuel Bamford, which passed in march-ing order, five abreast down Newton Lane and along Mosley Street, each leader with a sprig of peaceful laurel in his hat. Women and little ones preceded them, or ran on the footway, singing, dancing, shouting gleefully in the bright sunshine, as at any other pageant to which the music of the bugle gave life and spirit, and waving flags gave colour.

Once assembled, the scattered bands struck up 'God Save the King' and 'Rule Britannia', deafening shouts rent the air, and Henry Hunt, drawn in an open barouche by white horses, made his way slowly to the hustings amidst the enthusiastic cheering of the multitude.

Barely had Mr Hunt ascended the platform, taken off his white hat, and begun to address his attentive auditory, when there was a startling cry 'The soldiers are upon us!' and the 15th Hussars, galloping round a corner, came with their spare jackets flying loose, their sabres drawn, and threw themselves, men and horse, upon the closely packed mass, without a note of warning. All had been preconcerted, prearranged.

From the early morning, magistrates had been sitting at the Star Inn and there Hugh Birley, a cotton-spinner, was said to have regaled too freely the officers and men of his Yeomanry Corps, so soon to be let loose on the 'swinish multitude', as they called them.

A cordon of military and yeomanry had been drawn round St Peter's Field, like a horde of wolves round a flock of sheep. The borough reeve and other magistrates issued their orders from a house at the corner of Mount Street, which overlooked the scene; and thence (not from a central position, where he could be seen and heard) a clerical magistrate read the Riot Act from a window in an inaudible voice.

Then Nadin, the cowardly bully, having a warrant to apprehend the ringleaders – although he had a line of constables thence to the hustings – declared he *dared* not serve it without the support of the military.

His plea was heard; and thus, through the blindness, the incapacity, the cowardice, or the self-importance of this one man, soldiery hardened in the battlefield, Yeomanry fired with drink, were let loose like barbarians on a closely wedged mass of unarmed people, and one of the most atrocious massacres in history was the result.

Some questions for discussion

How could the attendance of wives and sweethearts 'serve as a guarantee of peaceable intention'?

Mrs Banks accuses a clerical magistrate of not reading the Riot

Act from a central position where he could be seen and heard. Can you think of any reason why the magistrate might have chosen to read it from the house rather than from a more central point?

Read the accounts which follow this extract. Does Mrs Banks's version strike you as a fair one?

Some writing topics

Imagine a young man from Middleton preparing himself for the early march to Manchester. He calls upon his sweetheart and the two of them join the main assembly. Describe these minutes *before* they leave Middleton.

We are often told how Henry Hunt was prevented from uttering anything but the first few words of his speech. Write out his speech, or part of it, as he might have delivered it had he been given the chance.

Imagine a scene in a Manchester inn before the meeting at St Peter's Field. A group of Yeomanry are drinking and talking. Describe their conversation until the time arrives for their departure.

Fame is the Spur

The following passage from *Fame is the Spur* by Howard Spring takes up the narrative from where Mrs Banks's account ends. In the opening chapter of this moving biographical novel, Old Warrior relates to the boy, Hamer Shawcross, how as a young man he had taken his sweetheart, Emma, to the meeting at St Peter's Field, Manchester. He tells of the gaiety and excitement they felt even though the occasion was a serious one and how, without warning or suspicion, the Yeomen charged, and in a few terrible minutes transformed their mood to one very near despair.

'We didn't know!' he cried. 'We never guessed!' But they knew then, with the grey rounded rumps of the horse pushing among them, with the sabres rising and falling.

'There were so many of us, we couldn't move, and they came at us like mad. I thought at first they were just trying to clear us out, till I heard a woman shriek and saw the blood rush out of her mouth as she opened it. Even with that, her mouth spouting red, she managed to shout: "Dragoons! Dragoons! Get Annie out of it!" and then she fell and they went over her.

'My God, the shrieks and yells! They came from all round us, and they came from the ground under our feet where poor devils had fallen and were being trampled by men and horses. I wasn't afraid . . . I was angry, not excited, but angry with a cold furious anger. I said to Emma: "Get behind me, luv. I'll shove a way out for you," and I was ready to smash and kill anyone who stopped me. "Keep hold of my coat, luv," I said, "an' then I'll know you're there," and I pushed on with my big oak stick in my hand.

'I pushed through everyone: bleeding men, and women with their clothes torn off them, and whimpering children, and wound-ed people down on their knees or flat on the ground. I wasn't thinking about any of them. It was hot, and the sweat was pouring into my eyes, and I was thinking: "A soldier! By Christ! Let me meet a soldier!"

'And there he was coming at us. The crowd had loosened. You could hear their wailing spreading out and away, and there was a clear space, and this soldier coming across it on a grey horse. I saw his empty scabbard clicking at his side, and the sabre red with blood in his hand, and I rushed to meet him shouting: "God damn you, you bastard! You're a poor man like us. What are you doing? What are you doing?"

'I waved my stick, and I could hear the leather creaking in the saddle and see the shine of his lovely boots. And then, when I was on him, his horse reared up, and I could see its front hoofs dang-ling over my head with the shoes gleaming, and the big veins in its belly. I struck upwards with my stick and hit the beast in the belly, and then Emma shrieked and pulled me backwards. I slipped on some blood and fell, and when the hoofs came pounding down I thought I was done for. But they missed me, and I lay there for a second with the dark arch of the horse over me, and then I saw the sabre sweeping past the side of the arch and a spurt of blood hit me in the face. Then the horse was gone, and there was Emma, lying on the ground.'

The old man's voice trembled. His hands trembled on the arms of the chair. 'She was dead. The blood was spurting out of her neck.'

He didn't speak for a moment, then he said simply: 'He had cut through her hair at the side of her head, the bit she had tied the ribbon on. I picked it up and put it in my pocket. There was nothing I could do for her then. I went to find the soldier.'

Some questions for discussion·

The Old Warrior says: 'I wasn't afraid. . . .' Why amid so much danger and violence was he not afraid?

As he pushes a way through the people, torn, bleeding and whimpering, he remarks: 'I wasn't thinking about any of them.' Does this mean he was indifferent to the suffering about him?

'God damn you, you bastard. You're a poor man like us!' Why does the man utter the second remark?

The old man tells how he picked up the ribbon worn by his dead sweetheart. 'There was nothing I could do for her then.' What was the significance for him of that simple ribbon?

Some writing topics

'I went to find the soldier.' Continue the story as the Old Warrior might have related it to the point where he arrives home at the end of the day.

Imagine the soldier who killed Emma returning home at evening, long after the crowds have been dispersed and the wounded and dead taken from the field. His wife, who has seen and heard nothing of the day's event's questions him as to what took place. Write their conversation in the form of a dialogue.

It has been estimated that well over sixty thousand people attended the Manchester meeting. Imagine that among them there was one blind man accompanied by a relative. Describe what he experienced on that day as told by himself. (Remember the extra importance of touch, sound and smell.)

The Courier

These 'fictional' versions of Peterloo are in fact very faithful accounts of what happened. The following description of the same event was given by a trained reporter who worked on a Manchester paper, *The Courier*. This extract, describes the scene as the Yeomanry charged:

As yet, I had seen, I had nothing to make the imagination of danger enter into my head. I had a constable at each elbow – constables all around me – in one moment more, however, I was fearfully undeceived. I heard the bugle sound – I saw the cavalry charge forward, sword in hand upon the multitude. I felt on the instant as if my heart had leaped from its seat. The woeful cry of dismay sent forth on all sides, the awful rush of so vast a living mass, the piercing shrieks of the women, the horrid confusion, are indescribable. I was carried forward almost off my feet, many yards nearer the hustings than I had been. I was running into the centre of the danger, but I could not help it – I had no choice – I had not a moment to choose. I found myself at last pushed up against the landau which brought Mr Hunt to the field. I know what rational hope I could have in seeking shelter under it, but under it I went, and coiled myself fast round the pole. A minute more, the cavalry were around me, trampling down and cutting all who could not get out of their way. I saw one or two persons trodden down close by me; one of them a constable, to whom

I had spoken half an hour before. A poor woman fell senseless at a few yards distance, under the cut of a sabre. Two country-men, regardless for a moment of their own safety, hastily raised her up, and brought her forward to the landau, into which they lifted her, and then hurried away.

A long conflict of voices now mingled itself with the clashing of swords and the groans of the wounded. I heard some person calling out 'Mr Hunt, I have a warrant against you'. Other voices 'At him, at him'. 'Murder, murder' – 'Mercy' – 'For God's sake, mercy'. I was particularly struck by hearing one person crying out in a voice of sore trouble: 'Protect *me*! Protect me! I am a privileged person – I am a reporter. I am the reporter of *The Courier*'. Would to God, thought I, you were only half as safe.

A loud crash, a confusing huzzaing, now announced to my astounded ears the capture of the party on the hustings, with their various colours and insignia; I thought this a fit moment for attempting my own escape, and, quitting my sulking place, got once more upon my feet. I ran at first, scarcely knowing what I did, towards a row of buildings called Windmill-street, but here the people, unable to get off, were tumbling over each other in heaps. The Yeomanry, after demolishing the hustings, were be-ginning to scatter themselves about, and were hewing down without mercy every person, man or woman, that came in their way. I saw more troops of cavalry pouring into the field, and the few avenues there were from the scene of bloodshed, choked with people, striving, many of them in vain, to effect their escape.

Some questions for discussion

The opening sentences of both this account and that of the Old Warrior make the same point. What is it? At what exact point did both witnesses unmistakably realize what was happening?

What part of the reporter's account clearly shows that the soldiers had lost control of the situation and were acting in confused panic?

Although the reporter is describing something which occurred weeks before writing his account, the passage reads as if it were actually happening in the present. How does he manage to achieve this 'present' effect though writing of the past?

Some writing topics

Imagine yourself a reporter at Peterloo. Describe as vividly as you can for your readers what you saw and heard at the Manchester meeting.

Much of the controversy which followed Peterloo concerned the actions of the Yeomanry. Write a letter to a local paper giving your point of view as to whether they behaved excusably or not.

One important fact about the assault upon the crowd at St Peter's field now needs explanation. Prior to the meeting two quite separate detachments of horsemen were awaiting their orders. The Yeomanry were made up of local small businessmen and traders, part-timers and amateurs, called in when the normal forces of law and order seemed likely to prove inadequate. They were untrained in crowd control and their horses unused to noise and excitement. The cavalry, on the other hand, were professional soldiers, many of them veterans of the Battle of Waterloo, fought four years earlier. The magistrates, who were watching the meeting from a near-by house, ordered the Yeomanry to enter the crowd and arrest the leaders on the rostrum. Unfortunately, they were not equal to the task and in the confusion which followed, the cavalry were ordered to go in and 'rescue' them.

The following account is by a Cavalry Lieutenant who took part in this rescue operation:

It was then for the first time that I saw the Manchester Troop of Yeomanry; they were scattered singly or in small groups over the greater part of the field, literally hemmed up and hedged into the mob so that they were powerless either to make an impression or to escape; in fact, they were in the power of those whom they were designed to overawe, and it required only a glance to discover their helpless position, and the necessity of our being brought to their rescue. As I was at the time informed, this hopeless state of things happened thus: A platform had been erected near the centre of the field, from which Mr Hunt and others were to address the multitude, and the magistrates having ordered a strong body of constables to arrest the speakers, unfortunately imagined that they should support the peace officers by bringing up the troop of Yeomanry at a walk. The result of this movement, instead of that which the magistrates desired, was unexpectedly to place this small body of horsemen (so introduced into a dense mob) entirely at the mercy of the people by whom they were, on all sides, pressed upon and surrounded.

The charge of the Hussars swept this mingled mass of human beings before it; people, yeomen, and constables, in their confused attempts to escape, ran one over the other; so that by the time we had arrived at the end of the field the fugitives were literally piled up to a considerable elevation above the level of the ground.

The Hussars drove the people forward with the flats of their swords, but sometimes, as is almost inevitably the case when men are placed in such situations, the edge was used, both by the Hussars, and, as I have heard, by the Yeomen also; but of this last part I was not cognisant, and believing though I do that nine out of ten of the sabre wounds were caused by the Hussars, I must still consider that it redounds to the humane forbearance of the men of the 15th that more wounds were not received, when the vast numbers are taken into consideration with whom they were brought into hostile collision; beyond all doubt, however, the far greater amount of injuries were from the pressure of the routed multitude.

Questions for discussion

Does this account put a different complexion upon the earlier reports of what happened at Manchester?

How reliable do you consider the Lieutenant's report? Is there any attempt to whitewash his own men?

Do you agree with the Lieutenant that 'it redounds to the humane forbearance of the men of the 15th that more wounds were not received'? (It has been estimated that a dozen people were killed at Peterloo and between five and six hundred wounded.)

Some writing topics

Imagine an encounter in a Manchester pub some days after Peterloo between a private in the Hussars and one of the yeomen now in civilian dress. You may like to write out their conversation in play-form.

Four distinct groups were involved in the Massacre of Peterloo: the magistrates, the Yeomanry, the Cavalry and the crowd. To what extent are each of these groups to blame for what occurred?

Passages in the Life of a Radical

For a final account of what happened at Peterloo we turn to Samuel Bamford, one of the leading Radicals of the time and a very competent writer and poet. His moving autobiography, *Passages in the Life of a Radical*, tells of the excitement he and his contingent felt as they entered Manchester from the outskirts of the town:

Having crossed Piccadilly, we went down Moseley Street, then almost entirely inhabited by wealthy families. We took the left side of St Peter's Church; and at this angle we wheeled quickly and steadily into Peter Street and soon approached a wide unbuilt space, occupied by an immense multitude, which opened and received us with loud cheers. We walked into that chasm of human beings, and took our station from the hustings across the causeway of Peter Street; and so remained, undistinguishable from without, but still forming an almost unbroken line, with our colours in the centre.

I ascended the hustings. Successive parties kept arriving on the ground, and we became deeper inclosed, until we occupied about the centre of that vast multitude.

In about half an hour after our arrival at the meeting, the sounds of music and reiterated shouts, proclaimed the near approach of Mr Hunt and his party; and in a minute or two they were seen coming from towards Deansgate, preceded by a band of music, and several flags. On the driving seat of a barouche sat a neatly dressed female supporting a small flag. Their approach was hailed by one universal shout from probably eighty thousand persons. They threaded their way slowly past us and through the crowd which Hunt eyed. The spectacle could not be otherwise in his view than solemnly impressive. Such a mass of human beings he had never beheld till then.

He mounted the hustings; the music ceased. Mr Hunt, stepping towards the front of the stage, took off his white hat, and addressed the people.

While he was doing so, I proposed to an acquaintance, that, as the speeches and resolutions were not likely to contain anything new to us, we should retire awhile and get some refreshment. He assented and we had got to nearly the outside of the crowd, when a noise and a strange murmur arose towards the church. Some persons said it was the Blackburn people coming; and I stood on tiptoe and looked in the direction whence the noise proceeded, and saw a party of cavalry in blue and white uniform, come trotting sword in hand, round the corner of a garden wall, and to the front of a row of new houses, where they reined up in a line.

'The soldiers are here,' I said, 'we must go back and see what this means.'

'Oh!' someone made reply, 'they are only come to be ready if there should be any disturbance in the meeting.'

'Well let us go back,' I said, and we forced our way towards the colours.

On the cavalry drawing up they were received with a shout, of goodwill, as I understood it. They shouted again, waving their sabres over their heads; and then, slackening rein, and striking spur into their steeds, they dashed forward cutting the people.

'Stand fast,' I said, 'they are riding upon us, stand fast.'

And there was a general cry in our quarter of 'Stand fast!' The cavalry were in confusion; they evidently could not, with all the weight of man and horse, penetrate that compact mass of human beings; and their sabres were plied to hew a way through naked held-up hands, and defenceless heads; and then chopped limbs, and wound gaping skulls were seen; and groans and cries were mingled with the din of that horrid confusion.

'Ah! ah!' 'For shame, for shame!' was shouted. Then 'Break! break! They are killing them in front, and they cannot get away'; and there was a general cry of, 'Break! break!'

For a moment the crowd held back as in a pause; then was a rush heavy and resistless as a headlong sea; and a sound like low thunder with screams, prayers, and imprecations, from the crowd-moiled, and sabre-doomed who could not escape.

On the breaking of the crowd, the Yeomanry wheeled; and dashing wherever there was an opening, they followed, pressing and wounding. Many females appeared as the crowd opened; and striplings or mere youths also were found. Their cries were piteous and heart-rending; and would, one might have supposed, dis-armed any human resentment; but here their appeals were in vain. Women, white-vested maids, and tender youths, were indis-criminately sabred or trampled.

In ten minutes from the commencement of the havoc, the field was an open and almost deserted space. The sun looked down through a sultry and motionless air. The hustings remained, with a few broken and hewed flag-staves erect, and a torn and gashed banner or two drooping; whilst over the whole field, were strewed caps, bonnets, hats, shawls, and shoes, and other parts of male and female dress; trampled, torn, and bloody. The Yeomanry had dismounted – some were easing their horses' girths, others adjusting their accoutrements; and some were wiping their sabres. Several mounds of human beings still remained where they had fallen, crushed down and smothered. Some of these still moaning – others with staring eyes, were gasping for breath, and others would never breathe more. All was silent save those low sounds, and the occasional snorting and pawing of steeds. Persons might sometimes be noticed peeping from attics fearful of being observed, or unable to sustain the full gaze of a scene so hideous and abhorrent.

Some questions for discussion

There is little agreement among either contemporary eye-witnesses or later historians as to how many people actually attended the Peterloo meeting. Bamford's estimate of eighty thousand persons may be accurate but it is probably high. If Bamford did err in his estimate why would he overestimate rather than underestimate the size of the crowd?

When the cavalry charged the cry went up, 'Stand fast!' Seconds later the cry changed to, 'Break, break!' How can you explain this rapid reversal of tactics?

Some writing topics

'We went down Mosley Street, then almost entirely occupied by wealthy families.' Imagine a conversation between a wealthy gentleman and his wife as they watched the passing procession of marchers on their way to St Peter's Field.

Imagine yourself the principal Radical speaker of the day, Henry Hunt. What were your opening remarks to the Peterloo assembly?

(Remember he was only able to utter a few sentences.) Go on to describe your thoughts and emotions as the cavalry charge and describe the scene as seen by you from the elevated rostrum.

Read each of these five accounts again carefully. Now write as accurate a report as you can on 'What really happened at Peterloo'.

The Mask of Anarchy

Some of England's most renowned poets were living at the time of Peterloo: Blake, Wordsworth, Coleridge, Southey, Byron, and Keats among them. Most of them felt passionately against the injustices of their time; a few were close friends of leading Radicals. The news of Peterloo reached Percy Bysshe Shelley in Italy. He had long advocated the reform of English society which he believed to exist solely for the exploitation of the masses by a few powerful and inhuman men. This latest outrage filled him with anger; it was the culmination of the Government's growing contempt for the ancient and elementary rights of Englishmen. He was convinced that those who had perpetrated the massacre were leading the country towards anarchy.

The poem is too long to include here in full, but Shelley's essential message is plain in these few verses:

> As I lay asleep in Italy
> There came a voice from over the sea,
> And with great power it forth led me
> To walk in the visions of Poesy.

> I met Murder on the way –
> He had a mask like Castlereagh –
> Very smooth he looked, yet grim;
> Seven bloodhounds followed him;

> All were fat; and well they might
> Be in admirable plight,
> For one by one and two by two,
> He tossed them human hearts to chew
> Which from his cloak he drew.

Next came Fraud, and he had on,
Like Eldon, an ermined gown;
His big tears, for he wept well,
Turned to mill-stones as they fell.

And the little children who
Round his feet played to and fro,
Thinking every tear a gem,
Had their brains knocked out by them.

Clothed with the Bible, as with light,
And the shadows of the night,
Like Sidmouth, next, Hypocrisy
On a crocodile rode by.

Last came Anarchy: he rode
On a white horse, splashed with blood;
He was pale even to the lips,
Like Death in the Apocalypse.

And a mighty troop around,
With their trampling shook the ground,
Waving each a bloody sword,
For the service of their Lord.

But Shelley does not end on a note of despair, for out of the tumult
arises Hope, in the image of a maiden, whose strength and innocence
encourage even the downcast to continue their fight.

And the prostrate multitude
Looked – and ankle deep in blood,
Hope, that maiden most serene,
Was walking with a quiet mien:

'Men of England, heirs of Glory,
Heroes of unwritten story,
Nurslings of one mighty Mother,
Hopes of her and one another;

'Rise like lions after slumber
In unvanquishable number
Shake your chains to earth like dew
Which in sleep has fallen on you –
Ye are many – they are few!'

The Massacre of Peterloo

The following poem was written by a 14-year-old girl in a Kent school. Marion's poem is based upon her experience of being in a production of *The Massacre of Peterloo* and describes what the last scene of the play meant for her.

The Yeomen charged down the grassy hill. The order was to kill.
'Kill the men, mothers and children too!'
This was the beginning of the end for Peterloo.

Horrified screams filled the air,
As people dropped dead everywhere.
The screams were heard for miles around
As one one by one they fell to the ground.

Sabres flashed bringing death and sorrow.
Would anyone live to see tomorrow?
Those who survived on that awful day
Cursed or prayed as they fled away.

When the noise of battle was spent
Men, women and children to the battlefield went,
And later on that dreadful day,
They helped to carry the dead away.

Deserted was the field except for five,
One was dead, the others alive.
Their heads bowed in sorrow, they lead the way
Samuel had died on this fateful day.

He fought for freedom, liberty and life.
How can we carry him *DEAD* to his wife?

The Massacre of Peterloo retells this story,
In a moving drama of death – not glory.
The audience wept to the bugle-call
And silent banners paraded the hall,
Told of the fight that is not yet won,
And the hope that cries: 'We shall Overcome!'

MARION HENLEY

Marion's poem is a sweeping description of the whole scene and doesn't set out to deal in any detail with particular aspects of the total event. You might like to compose a poem of a more closely focused character, concentrating on, for example:

The first sights and sounds as the cavalry approached.

An actual encounter between one of the crowd and a Yeoman.

The view of the charge as seen from the safety of a window in a near-by house.

The scene after the massacre as seen from the same window.

The experiences of a mother or father seeking a loved one soon after the massacre.

The death of a child at Peterloo.

Part III: Suggested Activities

Composing a folk-song

In an earlier part of this book (page 64) one of the finest industrial folk-songs appears. (There is an excellent rendering of this song on the record, 'The Iron Muse' produced by Topic Records Ltd.) You can compose your own folk-song based either on any of the Peterloo incidents or on working life in Manchester in 1819.

Reading Aloud

Voice production is of special importance in a play like *The Masasacre of Peterloo*. The play requires the clearest speaking of often quite lengthy passages. The impact of the crowd will be heightened if every pupil in it has practised delivery and enunciation. The following extracts from contemporary documents will provide suitable material for practice of this kind.

Reading the Riot Act

The Seditious Meetings and Assemblies Act, 1817, required that in the event of an illegal assembly forming 'the Justice of the Peace shall among the said persons assembled, with a loud voice, command or cause to be commanded silence; and after that shall openly and with a loud voice make a Proclamation in these words or like in effect:

> Our Sovereign Lord the King chargeth and commandeth all persons here assembled immediately to disperse themselves, and peaceably to depart to their habitations, or to their lawful business, upon Pain of Death. God Save the King!

The group might be asked to create a hubbub and the pupil chosen to read the Riot Act calls for silence. He then reads the relevant passage 'openly and with a loud voice'.

A Call to Arms

The use of arms or the urging of the use of them was, of course, rigorously forbidden at the time of Peterloo. Nevertheless, a notable Radical, J. T. Saxton, used a kind of incendiary language which must very nearly have qualified as illegal:

> I therefore call upon every man here present TO ARM HIMSELF with the powerful weapons of reason. TO PRESENT his firm remonstrance to the throne – and TO FIRE with the noble indignation of Britons determined to be free or die!

This should be read so as to stress the phrases in capital letters.

The Manchester Declaration

The great meeting at St Peter's Field was by no means the first, or indeed last, of its kind. In January 1819 the following declaration was read to a large assembly of Manchester workpeople:

> We make this our public and final declaration!
>
> That the only source of all legitimate power, is in the people, the whole people and nothing but the people!
>
> That all men are born free and equal!
>
> That taxation without representation is illegal, and ought to be abolished!
>
> That the Crown is a sacred trust and inheritance, held only by the free consent of the people!
>
> That according to the ancient Laws and Constitution of England every Freeman is entitled to a share in the Government of his country!

Each of these declarations may be greeted with loud and enthusiastic cheers.

The Lancashire Hymn

The following verses from Samuel Bamford's Lancashire Hymn lend themselves to choral speaking:

SOLO: Great God, who did of old inspire
         The patriot's ardent heart,
         And fill'd him with a warm desire
         To die, or do his part;

CHORUS: Oh! Let our shouts be heard by Thee,
         Genius great of liberty.

SOLO: And shall we tamely now forego
         The rights for which they bled?

> And crouch beneath a minion's blow,
> And basely bow the head?

CHORUS: Ah! no; it cannot, cannot be;
> Death for us, or liberty!

SOLO: Souls of our mighty sires, behold
> This band of brothers join.
> Oh never, never be it told,
> That we disgrace your line;

CHORUS: If England wills the glorious deed,
> We'll have another Runnimede.

These verses may also be sung to the tune of 'Almighty Father Strong to Save'.

Re-enacting the Trial of Henry Hunt and his Companions

Within a few months of the Peterloo meeting, Henry Hunt and his companions were tried and imprisoned for their part in convening 'an unlawful and seditious assembly'. The proceedings of the actual trial held in York are interesting enough though much of the discussion was of a legally technical character. Pupils might wish to stage their own trial basing their cases on the evidence derived from *The Massacre of Peterloo*. Pupils in the cast could play their same roles in the trial which should be staged as soon after the actual performances as possible so that memories of what took place are fresh.

The trial would comprise the two sides: Magistrates and Radicals. Hunt would be charged with 'the responsibility for the loss of life occasioned at St Peter's Field, Manchester, on August 16th 1819 as the result of the convening of an unlawful and seditious assembly'. The Radical case would claim that the meeting had not been prohibited, that those present behaved peaceably and that it was the magistrates in their nervousness and fear who gave the orders to send in the Yeomanry and the soldiers. The Magistrates, on the other hand, would argue that the forces of law and order in Manchester were inadequate and that they had a responsibility to protect the lives of the citizenry. They were alarmed by the sheer size of the meeting and what finally precipitated their decision to disperse the meeting by force was the action of removing the rostrum from the end of the gangway deliberately designed to give access to the Radical leaders. In considering whether the meeting was seditious in character a wider discussion could develop in which the social and political conditions of the time are educed by way of evidence. If pupils carefully prepared themselves the trial might prove almost as valuable as the play. Witnesses could base their evidence on the material at the beginning of this section, on their own reading and research and on their own imaginative interpretation of what occurred. A jury would pronounce Hunt guilty or innocent at the end of the trial. (Of course there is no reason why the magistrates should not be charged rather than the Radicals.) Some children might act as reporters and write up accounts of what transpires.

Further Topics for Discussion and Writing

(1) Most of the workers at Peterloo were practising Christians. From the chapels of Lancashire they gained education for their children at Sunday-school, companionship, and often leadership, for themselves. On the whole they were Nonconformists, Baptists or Methodists. Those who could read would have read Bunyan's *Pilgrim's Progress;* many would have heard Wesley give one of his rousing sermons. Read parts of Bunyan's masterpiece and explain why the book had such an enormous appeal among ordinary working people in the early nineteenth century. What did Wesley's Methodism offer the poor? Why were the poor never strongly joined to the Church of England?

(2) In Part One of the Play there is an extract from a sermon actually delivered by a Manchester clergyman at the time of Peterloo. He is telling Samuel in effect that Christians should not get mixed up in politics. In 1920 the Anglican Bishops issued the following resolution:

An outstanding and pressing duty of the Church is to convince its members of the necessity of nothing less than a fundamental change in the spirit and working of our economic life. . . . All Christians ought to take an active part in bringing about this change, by which alone we can hope to remove class dissentions and resolve industrial discords.

What evidence can you find in the New Testament which shows what advice Christ might have given on the subject of reform had he lived in a modern industrial State.

(3) Samuel Coppitt tells his Radical visitors: 'God didn't mean us to tolerate cruelty and injustice either.' In order to decide what the Christian can do about cruelty and injustice, consider the lives of the following great Christians; William Wilberforce, Cardinal Manning, Dietrich Bonhoeffer, and Martin Luther King. What evils faced them? How did they deal with them?

(4) *The Massacre of Peterloo* involves a number of conflicts in personal relationships. What were the differences of view between the following characters? Comment in each case on how you feel about the way in which the difference was resolved.

Between Samuel and Martha over whether Samuel should go to the meeting or not.

Between Tom and Kate about whether they should marry or not.

Between the women of the Female Reform Society as to Mrs Cranford's offer of charity soup.

Between General Byng and Norris over the question of the employment of spies and the way to handle demonstrators.

Between the soldier and his own inner voice. Are orders as clean-cut as he suggests or should he have argued and acted differently? Between Hulton and Norris about the question of legality? (Are there occasions when expediency is more important?) How might Hulton have resisted Norris's domination?

(5) Demonstrations and protests are as rife today as they were 150 years ago, and in the same way there is considerable disagreement between different groups taking part as to whether violence should or should not be used. If you felt strongly against some injustice would you ever attempt to gain your end by the use of force or the destruction of property?

(6) The Peterloo marchers were convinced that they were as entitled to the vote as anyone else because they felt they mattered as much as anyone else. Do workers matter as much as wealthy or important people? Why do they earn less? In what ways are people equal? and not equal?

(7) Imagine yourself secretary of a political group who wish to organize an open-air meeting. What does the law require you to do before you attempt to organize such a meeting. Why do demonstrations and meetings seldom end today in the kind of tragedy which occurred in Manchester in 1819?

(8) On what subjects do people feel sufficiently strong today to march, demonstrate, petition, and protest? With which of these causes, if any, do you have sympathy? Are there any with which you strongly disagree?

(9) Englishmen often pride themselves on their freedom of speech. Does this mean that you can say or write anything you like for other people to hear or read? What laws place limits on freedom of speech?

(10) Read D. H. Lawrence's poem, 'A Sane Revolution'. Write an imaginary conversation between Lawrence and a Peterloo marcher who disagrees with the main argument in the poem.

Personal Folios

Some pupils may wish to compose their own folios based on the Peterloo theme. These folios might contain material from the rest of this section along with illustrations, personal research and imaginative work. Here are a few suggestions for themes. A book-list is appended which may be of help.

Biography

(1) Your folio tells the life-story of one of the characters in the play, perhaps the one played by you. Although much of your biography will have to be imaginative, you can gain a great deal of information by studying the lives of the ordinary people of whom he or she is typical.

(2) The life-story of one of the real people mentioned in the play or in this pupils' section, e.g. Henry Hunt, Samuel Bamford, Tom Paine, William Cobbett, Thomas Hardy.

Manchester Then and Now

(3) What sort of town was Manchester in 1819? (Include maps and illustrations.) How did the poor and rich live? What were their opportunities for leisure and recreation? Contrast this Manchester with that of modern times.

The March of Freedom

(4) Trace the steps by which political and social freedom were established in this country. Start at 1819 and give to each a banner-heading, e.g.; 1824, COMBINATION LAWS REPEALED: TRADES UNIONS LEGALIZED. 1829, PEEL'S MODERN POLICE FORCE CREATED, etc. Accompany each of these headings with a note of explanation. This work would be of great value as a contribution to the final scene when members of the cast parade with banners commemorating notable advances in the progress towards freedom.

Costume

(5) Providing costumes for as large a cast as that required in *The Massacre of Peterloo* is a huge undertaking. Most of the cast will no doubt be asked to make their own costumes. It would be of great help if members of the crowd had four simple models to work from; costumes for a man, woman, boy and girl. Make full-size sketches of these four basic designs along with instructions on how they could be cheaply and quickly made. You may also like to draw the

costumes worn by a Manchester gentleman and lady, a yeoman, a
clergyman and a Hussar.

Book lists

Books which pupils at CSE or equivalent level might find helpful:

Pauline Gregg, *A Social and Economic History of Britain, 1760–1955.*
H. Fagan, *The Unsheathed Sword;* 'Champions of the Workers'.
The *Jackdaw* Folio on *Peterloo.*
T. A. Jackson, *Trials of British Freedom.*
Donald Read, *Peterloo.*
R. J. White, *Waterloo to Peterloo.*

Each of these contain accounts of the massacre.

Books of a specialist interest to teachers and more senior pupils:

Tom Paine, *The Rights of Man.*
C. Gill, *The Naval Mutinies of 1797.*
G. D. H. Cole, *Life of Cobbett.*
William Cobbett, *Rural Rides.*
Moncure Conway, *Tom Paine.*
C. R. Fay, *Life and Labour in the Nineteenth Century.*
Ivy Pinchbeck, *Women Workers in the Industrial Revolution.*
E. Halevy, *England in 1815.*
E. P. Thompson, *The Making of the English Working Class.*
J. L. and Barbara Hammond, *The Skilled Labourer, 1760–1832.*
Samuel Bamford, *Passages in the Life of a Radical.*
Sir Charles Oman, *The Unfortunate Colonel Despard.*
H. W. C. Davis, *Lancashire Reformers, 1816–17.*
F. A. Bruton, *The Story of Peterloo.*
Frank Peel, *The Rising of the Luddites.*